Collins

New GCSE Maths
Multistep and Problem Solving Skills

Chris Pearce

William Collins' dream of knowledge for all began with the publication of his first book in 1819. A self-educated mill worker, he not only enriched millions of lives, but also founded a flourishing publishing house. Today, staying true to this spirit, Collins books are packed with inspiration, innovation and practical expertise. They place you at the centre of a world of possibility and give you exactly what you need to explore it.

Collins. Freedom to teach.

Published by Collins
An imprint of HarperCollins*Publishers*
77–85 Fulham Palace Road
Hammersmith
London
W6 8JB

© HarperCollins*Publishers* Limited 2013

10 9 8 7 6 5 4 3 2 1

ISBN-13 978-0-00-752040-4

Chris Pearce asserts his moral right to be identified as the author of this work.

British Library Cataloguing in Publication Data.
A Catalogue record for this publication is available from the British Library.

Commissioned by Katie Sergeant
Edited and proofread by Joan Miller
Design and typesetting by Jouve India Private Limited
Illustrations by Ann Paganuzzi
Cover design by Angela English
Production by Rebecca Evans

Printed and bound by L.E.G.O S.p.A Italy

Browse the complete Collins catalogue at:
www.collinseducation.com

Acknowledgements
The publishers wish to thank the following for permission to reproduce photographs. Every effort has been made to trace copyright holders and to obtain their permission for the use of copyright material. The publishers will gladly receive any information enabling them to rectify any error or omission at the first opportunity.

Cover image: Abstract background with number File404 © shutterstock.com

Contents

Introduction

Here are two GCSE examination questions.

1. (a) Simplify $3s - 5t - 2s - 4t$.

   (b) Factorise $6y - 15$.

   (c) Expand and simplify $2r + 3(2 - r)$.

2. Sally works as an engineer and earns £42 000 each year.
   30% of her monthly pay is deducted each month for tax and other items.
   How much is left each month after the deductions?

These are different **types** of question.

Question 1 is straightforward. This question tests whether you can remember the meaning of words such as *simplify* and *factorise* and show that you can do it correctly. *Straightforward* is not the same as *easy*. You may find this question difficult or easy but it is clear that it is an algebra question. It is testing skills that you should have learnt.

Question 2 is different. It describes a real situation and asks a question, set within a context. It does not tell you what you have to do – you have to work that out for yourself. There are different ways to work out the answer and each of them will have several steps. You have not been given any hints to guide you. Some of the information you have been given is not required to answer the question.

Your GCSE exam will include **both** types of question. This book is about questions of the second type, like question 2.

Question 2 is a **multistep** question because you need to make several calculations to reach the answer. It is also a **problem-solving** question because the question is in a particular context. In this case it is a real-life context but it could also have been a mathematical one.

You can recognise multistep questions in an examination because they will generally have 4, 5 or 6 marks and not be divided into separate sections. You can recognise problem-solving questions because they will be in a context or look less specific than the more 'usual' questions, like question 1. As you saw with question 2, a question can be both a multistep one and a problem-solving one.

Fortunately the techniques for solving multistep questions and problem-solving questions are the same and you do not need to worry which it is or whether it is both. For that reason, from now on we shall simply refer to them both **problem-solving questions**.

First we shall look in more detail at the type of question you could be asked and the strategies you can use to answer them. Then we shall do some worked examples, explaining each step we take to solve a problem. After that, there are lots of questions for you to try for yourself.

PROBLEM-SOLVING QUESTIONS

Questions may be set that:

- are mathematical problems or relate to the 'real world'
- are unfamiliar and not routine questions that you have seen before
- can be solved in more than one way
- have solutions that are useful or have a point.

You may be expected to:

- decide what mathematical knowledge will be useful
- choose a strategy to solve a problem
- decide what information is relevant and useful
- explain the method you used
- give a reason to justify a statement
- write your answers clearly.

Now look again at question 2 with this in mind.

- Sally works as an engineer and earns £42 000 each year.
- 30% of her monthly pay is deducted each month for tax and other items.
- How much is left each month after the deductions?

This is a question that relates to the 'real world'. Read the question carefully.

What do you know?

- Earns £42 000 each year.
- Deduct 30% each month.
- The fact that Sally is an engineer is irrelevant.

What do you need to find out?

- How much is left, after deductions, each month

What strategy could you try?

This is a question about percentages. Notice where it says *year* and where it says *month*. Make sure you answer the right question!

Now think about the steps you might need to take to solve the problem. Do not answer it yet – just think about how to do it. Can you think of **different ways** to solve it? Think about that before you read on.

Here are three different methods. How many did you think of?

Method 1: Find 30% of 42 000. Subtract that from 42 000. Divide the answer by 12.

Method 2: Divide 42 000 by 12. Find 30% of the answer. Subtract that from the previous answer.

Method 3: Find 70% of 42 000. Divide the answer by 12.

Did you think of any others?

All these methods are correct and you can use any of them.

In an exam you do not need to find more than one method. This is just an example to show that different methods may be possible. It is a good idea to show any calculations you make so that if you make a mistake in the arithmetic you can still be given marks for your method.

Which bullet points at the start of this section apply to this question?

PROBLEM-SOLVING STRATEGIES

There is no set of rules that apply to every problem-solving question. You cannot say 'always do this'. However, there are some guidelines that might help.

1. **Read the question carefully.** It is surprising how often in examinations students give an incorrect answer because they have not read the question properly.

2. **What have you been asked to do?** Look for key words such as **find**, **work out**, **calculate**, **describe**, **explain** or **prove**.

3. **What information have you been given?** You can underline or highlight things on your question paper or you can write down important points. If a question is set in a 'real-life' context you will need to pick out the important information that will help you solve the problem.

4. **Where is the maths?** Is this a question about number or algebra? Geometry or statistics? What mathematical tools will you be using? Look for clues in the question.

5. **Can you see a way to tackle the problem?** If not, can you see a way to get started? There is usually something you can do and this might lead you on to the answer. Do not be afraid to try something just because it might not work.

6. **Show your working.** Write down anything you do. Even if you cannot solve the problem completely you might still get marks for a partial answer or a correct method – but only if the person marking the paper can see it!

7. **Check your answer.** Does it seem reasonable? Have you put in units? Have you rounded it sensibly, if necessary? If you were asked for an explanation, read through it carefully and make sure it makes sense.

8. **Look at the marks available.** If there are only two marks then do not spend too long on it. If there are five or six then it will be worth spending more time. Remember that there will be marks for method and for a partial answer.

PROBLEM-SOLVING LANGUAGE

This is a guide to words you might find in problem-solving questions in a GCSE examination. These words can be a guide to the sort of answer that is required.

Knowing what the words mean will help you to achieve the best possible mark.

Similar types of instruction are grouped together.

What it says	Examples	What it means
Work out	Work out the cost of the whole journey. Work out the smallest possible angle.	This is straightforward. There is a calculation to be done. You should always show your calculations, even if you are not asked to. That way you can still get method marks, even if your answer is incorrect.
Find	Find the missing length. Find the value of F.	Similar to 'work out'. There may be more than one way to get the answer. If the question does not tell you to use a particular method, then any valid method must get full marks.
Calculate	Calculate the volume of the cuboid.	This indicates that a calculator will be necessary or useful.
Estimate	Estimate the area of the field. Estimate the number of accidents that will happen in the next week.	In this case you are not expected to give an exact answer. For example, if you are finding an area by counting squares it will only be approximately correct. You can use a probability to estimate the number of accidents but you cannot know an exact number.
Calculate/work out the length/area/ mass/volume …	Find the length of the third side of the triangle. Calculate the volume of the barrel.	When you are asked to work out measurements you will probably need to round your answer. Look at the other numbers in the question as a guide. If the lengths of two sides of a triangle are 5.8 cm and 6.3 cm, it would be a mistake to say the third one is 4.910 385 6 cm because that is the answer on your calculator. Round it to 4.9 cm. Always put units in your answer.
The exact value	Find the exact value of x.	In a mathematical problem you may want a precise answer such as $\sqrt{3}$ or 2π. If an exact answer is required then writing 1.732 or 6.28 would not be correct in this case.
Show	Show that the total cost is £57 000. Show your working.	You must write down any calculations you do. You should always do that anyway but in this case you will lose marks if you do not.
Prove	Prove that the square of an even number is always a multiple of 4.	This is a stronger version of 'show'. It usually means you need to use algebra and set out the steps of your answer very clearly.
Explain	Explain how you know. Explain how you got your answer.	A bit like 'show' but in this case words will be required. You do not need to write a lot, often just a phrase or sentence is enough. Something like 'the angles of a triangle add up to 180°' or 'alternate angles' could be sufficient. Try to use the correct mathematical words and notation.

What it says	Examples	What it means
Give a reason	Is the triangle isosceles? Give a reason for your answer.	This is similar to 'explain'. An answer of 'yes' or 'no' will not be enough and you will have to justify your answer.
Describe fully	Describe fully the transformation that maps shape A onto shape B.	This is often used for transformations. A reflection needs a mirror line; a rotation must have a centre, an angle and a direction; a translation needs a vector.
Words in bold type	What is the probability she will **not** be late?	The examiner is trying to help you by highlighting particular words. Look at those words with particular care.
Compare	Compare the marks of the two groups of students.	You will often see this in data-handling questions. You can compare two things by finding similarities or differences. An example would be to find the average values and say something about them. Are they the same? Which is larger? Look at the number of marks available. That is a clue to how much you need to say.
As simply as possible	Write the answer as simply as possible. Simplify your answer as much as possible.	You will often see this if the answer is a fraction or a ratio. You should be able to simplify both. It is a good idea to simplify fractions and ratios as much as possible, even if you are not explicitly asked to do so.
Write down	Write down the factors of 10.	This means there are no method marks. You will only get marks for the correct answer.
Average	Find the average length.	You should know about three averages: the mean, the median and the mode. Make sure you know when it is best to use each one.
Not drawn accurately		If you see this next to a diagram it means you cannot measure lengths or angles on it. Your values will not be accurate.

WORKED EXAMPLES

In this section you will see a number of questions and their solutions. The comments will help you to see how to tackle problems, how to set out your answers and how marks are awarded. M means a method mark and A means an answer mark. So M1A1 means 2 marks altogether, one for the method and another for using it to get the correct answer.

Many GCSE examinations award marks for *quality of written communication* (QWC). In mathematics this means you use the correct notation and vocabulary. You should also use correct spelling, punctuation and grammar in any explanation you are asked for. In these worked examples you will see QWC where this is being specifically assessed.

One worked example is marked as Foundation only. One is marked as Higher only. The rest could be Foundation or Higher.

WORKED EXAMPLE 1 (FOUNDATION ONLY)

A circular spinner has 20 sectors of equal size.

Each sector is one of four colours, red, green, blue or yellow.

The probability the pointer stops on red is $\frac{1}{4}$.

The probability the pointer stops on green is $\frac{2}{5}$.

The probability the pointer stops on blue is $\frac{3}{10}$.

How many sectors are yellow?   **(4 marks)**

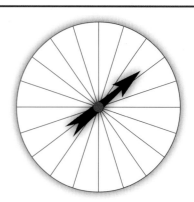

SOLUTION

The number of red sectors is $\frac{1}{4}$ of 20 = 5.

The number of green sectors is $\frac{2}{5}$ of 20 = 8.

The number of red sectors is $\frac{3}{10}$ of 20 = 6.

So the number of yellow sectors is
$20 - (5 + 8 + 6) = 1$

What do you know? The probability can be used to find the number of sectors of each colour.

M1A1

M1A1

WORKED EXAMPLE 2

A school is planning a trip for the students.

The school has booked three coaches that can hold 47, 51 and 52 passengers respectively.

The ratio of teachers to students must be at least 1 : 8.

What is the largest number of students that can go on the trip?   **(4 marks)**

SOLUTION

Altogether there are $47 + 51 + 52 = 150$ seats

1 teacher can take 8 students = 9 seats
2 teachers can take 16 students = 18 seats
3 teachers can take 24 students = 27 seats ...

What do we know? The number of seats and the ratio.

What do we want to find? The maximum number of students.

You could carry on like this until you reach 150 but there is a quicker way.

How many groups of 9 are there? *A group of 9 is 1 teacher and 8 students.*

$150 \div 9 = 16.66...$

Round that down to 16.

$16 \times 8 = 128$

16 teachers can take 128 students and that uses 144 seats. *M1A1 for whichever method you use.*

There are 6 seats left. *Don't forget to fill those seats too.*

You can take 1 teacher + 5 students.

That is a maximum of $128 + 5 = 133$ students. *M1A1 for the extra seats.*

WORKED EXAMPLE 3

In a youth club there are 20% more girls than boys.

What is the ratio of girls to boys? **(4 marks)**

SOLUTION

Either

Suppose there are 20 boys.

We know there are more girls than boys but we do not know the numbers.

One method is to choose a number of boys to start with. Any convenient number will do.

20% of $20 = \frac{1}{5}$ of 20

$= 4$ *M1*

There are 24 girls. *A1*

The ratio of boys to girls

$= 20 : 24$ *M1*

$= 5 : 6$ *A1 QWC for simplifying as much as possible.*

Or *Another method is to use algebra.*

Suppose there are N boys.

20% of N is $0.2N$ *M1A1*

The number of girls is $N + 0.2N = 1.2N$

The ratio of boys to girls is $N : 1.2N$ *Multiply 1 and 1.2 by 5 to make whole numbers.*

$= 1 : 1.2 = 5 : 6$

M1A1QWC

Either method can get full marks.

WORKED EXAMPLE 4

Ashley is writing the odd numbers in four columns.

He starts like this.

1	3	5	7
9	11	13	15
17	19	21	23
25	27	29	31

He keeps adding more rows in the same way.

(a) What is the 20th number in the first column?

(b) Explain why 1001 must be in the first column.

(4 marks)

SOLUTION

(a) The numbers in the first column are:

   1   9   17   25   ...   ...

What do you know? It is the numbers in the first column you are interested in.

It continues 33, 41, ... Adding 8 each time.

Look for a pattern. M1

Compare the sequence with the multiples of 8.

It will be useful to find the nth term.

1	9	17	25	33	...
8	16	24	32	40	...

The nth term is $8n - 7$.
The 20th term is $8 \times 20 - 7 = 153$

M1A1

You could also get this answer by repeatedly adding 8 until you get to the 20th term.

(b) Could the nth term be 1001?

*Use the formula from part (**a**).*

$8n - 7 = 1001 \Rightarrow 8n = 1008 \Rightarrow n = 126$
1001 is in the first column.
It is the 126th term.

M2A1 You need a clear explanation to get full marks.

This is more difficult if you do not have the formula.

Notice that you did not need all the numbers in the table, only the first column.

WORKED EXAMPLE 5

Lines P and Q are parallel.

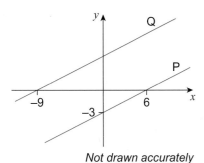

Not drawn accurately

Work out the equation of line Q.

(4 marks)

SOLUTION

What do you know? Three points where the lines cross the axes (the fourth is missing). The lines are parallel.

The equation of a straight line is in the form $y = mx + c$ where m is the gradient.

This is the maths you will use.

Need to find the gradient of Q.

The gradient of P is $\frac{3}{6} = \frac{1}{2}$ or 0.5.

Line Q is parallel to P so it has the same gradient.

You cannot find the gradient of Q directly but you can find the gradient of P. M1A1

The equation of Q is $y = 0.5x + c$.
$(-9, 0)$ is on the line so $0 = 0.5 \times -9 + c$
$\Rightarrow c = 4.5$
The equation of Q is $y = 0.5x + 4.5$.

You could also use similar triangles to find where Q crosses the y-axis.
M1A1

WORKED EXAMPLE 6

Sam writes down five consecutive positive integers.

She finds that the sum of the five numbers is a multiple of five.

Show that this is always the case, whatever positive integers she chooses.

(4 marks)

SOLUTION

What do you know? You have five consecutive integers. A simple example is 1, 2, 3, 4, 5.

The sum of these is 15, which is a multiple of 5 (it is 5 × 3).

To show it is true for any five numbers needs algebra.

Suppose the numbers are N, $N + 1$, $N + 2$, $N + 3$ and $N + 4$.

The sum is: $N + (N + 1) + (N + 2) + (N + 3) + (N + 4)$

$= 5N + 15$

$= 5(N + 3)$

which is a multiple of 5 for any value of N.

Because they are consecutive you only need one letter for an unknown. M1A1

Factorising shows that the sum is a multiple of 5. M1A1 QWC

This is not the only way to do it.

For example, if the middle number was N, the others would be $N - 2$, $N - 1$, $N + 1$ and $N + 2$. What is the sum of the five numbers, in this case?

WORKED EXAMPLE 7

Each of these diagrams is made up of rectangles of the same size.

The perimeter of the first one is 38 cm.

The perimeter of the second one is 54 cm.

Find the perimeter of the third one.

(5 marks)

Not drawn accurately

SOLUTION

You know the perimeter of the first two diagrams – this is the distance round the outside.

If you can find the size of each small rectangle you can find the perimeter of the third diagram.

Suppose l cm and w cm are the length and width of each rectangle.

$4l + 2w = 38$

$6l + 2w = 54$

The difference between them is:

$2l = 16$

So $l = 8$

Now substitute this in the first equation:

$32 + 2w = 38$

So $w = 3$

The perimeter of the third diagram is:

$2l + 6w$

$= 16 + 18 = 34$ cm

Use letters to stand for the unknown lengths

M1

One perimeter is 2 'rectangle lengths' longer than the other. A1

Can see this if you write 8 on each rectangle length in the first diagram.

A1

You can see the perimeter is 2 'lengths' and 6 'widths'. M1

A1

You could do this without using algebra and still get all the marks.

WORKED EXAMPLE 8

Pete is making a circular ring from a rectangular strip of paper.

To do this, he will stick a 2 cm section at one end of the strip over a 2 cm section at the other end of the strip.

The diameter of the circular ring will be 10 cm.

How long is the rectangular strip of paper?

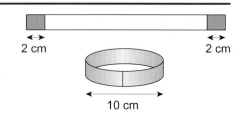

Not drawn accurately

(4 marks)

SOLUTION

The diameter of the circle is 10 cm.

You have a circle with a diameter of 10 cm. Start with that.

The circumference is $\pi \times 10 = 31.4$ cm

If you want the length of the strip you need to find the circumference of the circle. You should know the formula. M1A1

When the strip of paper is made into a circle there is a 2 cm overlap.
The length of the strip is $31.4 + 2$

Think carefully about how much extra length you need.

$= 33.4$ cm

M1A1.
Round the answer sensibly. To the nearest mm is best. You could not measure more accurately than that with a ruler.

WORKED EXAMPLE 9

A football is made from 32 leather panels.

12 panels are regular pentagons. 20 panels are regular hexagons.

Here is part of the net of a football.

Work out the size of the angle marked $a°$.   **(5 marks)**

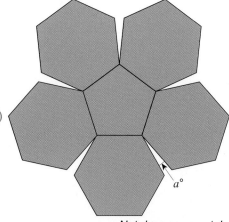

Not drawn accurately

SOLUTION

The angles of a pentagon add up to $3 \times 180°$ $= 540°$.

What do you know? These are regular polygons. You should be able to find the angles.

Each angle is $540° \div 5 = 108°$.

M1A1

The angles of a hexagon add up to $4 \times 180° = 720°$.

Each angle is $720° \div 6 = 120°$.

A1

The angles round a point add up to $360°$.

$120 + 120 + 108 + a = 360$

$a = 12$

These are the four angles at the point where one angle is marked $a°$.

M1A1

Notice that you did not need the facts about the number of panels in a football to solve the problem.

WORKED EXAMPLE 10

In the board game *Monopoly*™ each player throws two dice and adds the scores together.

Players can 'get out of jail' if they throw 7, 11 or doubles.

What is the probability of a player 'getting out of jail'?   **(5 marks)**

SOLUTION

This table shows the possible totals that can be scored with two dice.

+	1	2	3	4	5	6
1	2	3	4	5	6	7
2	3	4	5	6	7	8
3	4	5	6	7	8	9
4	5	6	7	8	9	10
5	6	7	8	9	10	11
6	7	8	9	10	11	12

How can you get 7, 11 or doubles with two dice? You need a sensible way to find all the possible scores.

You could use a table, a grid or an ordered list. Any method will get the marks.

M1A2

7s and 11s are circled.

Doubles have squares round them.

14 outcomes out of 36 will 'get out of jail'.

The probability is $\frac{14}{36} = \frac{7}{18}$.

Remember that a probability must be a fraction, a percentage or a decimal.

M1A1

WORKED EXAMPLE 11

This table shows the times of the runners in the Surrey men's cross-country championship in 2013.

Time (minutes)	Frequency	Time (minutes)	Frequency
40–	13	65–	2
45–	38	70–	3
50–	58	75–	0
55–	38	80–	2
60–	18	85–90	1

Imagine you have been asked to write a report about the race.

(a) Draw a diagram to summarise the results that could be in your report.

(b) Find one statistic that would be useful in your report.

(6 marks)

SOLUTION

(a) Either a histogram

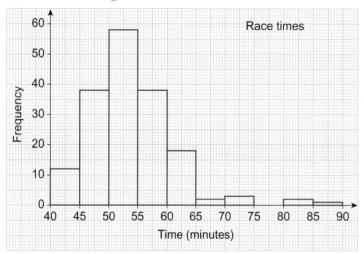

The data is continuous. The best diagram is a histogram or a cumulative frequency curve (Higher only). Either will get full marks. Do not draw both!

A bar chart or a pie chart is not a good choice.

M1 for choice of diagram.

A1 for correctly labelled axes.

A2 for correct heights or points QWC.

or a cumulative frequency curve.

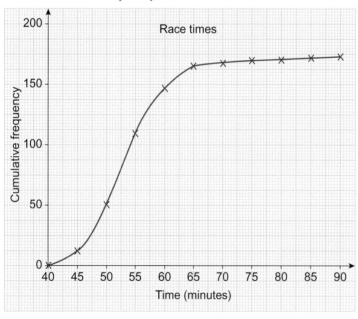

The plotted points should be (40, 0), (45, 13), (50, 51), (55, 109), (60, 147), (65, 165), (70, 167), (75, 170), (80, 170), (85, 172), (90, 173).

Higher level only: you could group the classes with longer times if you wish and use frequency density on the vertical axis but it is not necessary to get the marks.

(b) One of:

the modal class is 50–55 minutes

or the median time is about 53 minutes

or the mean is approximately 53.9 minutes.

M1 for choosing a suitable statistic.

A1

The mean takes a long time to work out so you may prefer to use a different statistic if you have a choice.

WORKED EXAMPLE 12 (HIGHER ONLY)

The field of vision of a pair of binoculars can be given in two ways.

1 As the angle that can be seen through the binoculars.

2 As the width, in metres, that can be seen at a distance of 1000 metres.

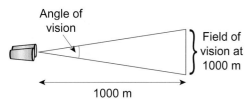

The field of vision of a pair of binoculars is 5.5°.

What is the width of the field of vision at 1000 metres?   **(5 marks)**

SOLUTION

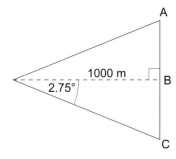

$\tan 2.75° = \frac{AB}{1000}$

$AB = 1000 \times \tan 2.75°$

$\quad = 48.0$

$AC = 2 \times AB = 2 \times 48.0$

$\quad = 96.0 \text{ m}$

What do you know? Being given an angle, a distance and a triangle suggests a trigonometry question.

It is a good idea to draw a diagram.

The triangle is isosceles. The line through the middle gives a right-angled triangle.

M1

Use the tangent ratio M1A1

A1

A1

Number

1. These are the ingredients in a recipe to make 12 cookies.

50 g almonds

50 g butter

3 tablespoons plain flour

100 g caster sugar

2 tablespoons whipping cream

$\frac{1}{2}$ teaspoon vanilla essence

Work out how much of each ingredient you need to make 30 cookies.   **(4 marks)**

2. Sam is 14 years old.

She goes to a football match with her father.

They sit in the West Stand.

Seat Prices	
Adults	
Pavilion Stand	£21.00
North Stand	£16.50
West Stand	£12.50
Hill Stand	£11.00
Under 16 years old	
All areas	£ 5.25

Snack bar prices	
Soft drinks	£1.85
Tea	£1.50
Coffee	£2.25
Pasties	£3.89
Pies	£2.79

At half time Sam has a soft drink.

Her father has tea and a pasty.

Find the total cost of their trip.   **(3 marks)**

3. Look at this grid.

	Multiple of 6	Multiple of 10
Multiple of 8		
Multiple of 12		

Write the **smallest** possible positive integer in each cell.   **(4 marks)**

4. Here are four digits.

3   5   6   7

Use each digit once to write down a number as close as possible to 6000.   **(3 marks)**

5. Ruth is buying the components to make a bookcase.

This is the plan she has drawn.

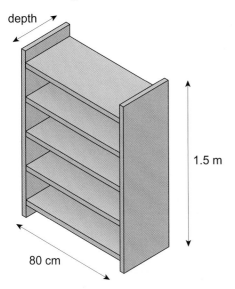

depth

1.5 m

80 cm

She needs to buy **shelves** and **uprights**.

Shelves and uprights are available in different lengths and depths.

Here is a price list.

Prices are in pounds (£)		Shelves		Uprights		
		40 cm	**80 cm**	**1.2 m**	**1.5 m**	**1.8 m**
Depth	**18 cm**	10.50	14.70	19.95	22.04	27.31
	24 cm	11.55	16.80	21.00	23.10	28.35
	30 cm	13.64	19.95	30.44	31.50	36.75

Ruth chooses shelves with a depth of 30 cm.

Work out the total cost.   **(5 marks)**

6. This is a mileage table.

It shows the shortest distances between cities, by road.

For example, the shortest distance by road between Oxford and Cambridge is 82 miles.

Alicia lives in Nottingham.

On one day she wants to drive to Peterborough and Northampton and then return home.

Work out her shortest driving distance.   **(3 marks)**

Cambridge

150	Gloucester				
56	79	Northampton			
86	107	64	Nottingham		
82	48	44	102	Oxford	
37	139	45	58	86	Peterborough

7. Four people are buying tickets for an airline flight.

> ### Price list
>
> | Ticket | £24.50 per person |
> |---|---|
> | Luggage | £11.75 for each item |
> | Booking fee | £4.95 per person |
> | Credit card fee | £3.25 |

Three of them have one piece of luggage each.

The fourth has no luggage.

Each has to pay a booking fee.

They all pay on the same credit card.

Work out the total cost.   **(4 marks)**

8. This table shows the cost of sending letters and packets in the UK.

Weight	First class	Second class
Letter		
0–100 g	60p	50p
Large letter		
0–100 g	90p	69p
101–250 g	£1.20	£1.10
251–500 g	£1.60	£1.40
501–750 g	£2.30	£2.90
Packet		
0–750 g	£2.70	£2.20
751–1000 g	£4.30	£2.50
1001–1250 g	£5.60	Items heavier than 1000 g cannot be sent second class.
1251–1500 g	£6.50	
1501–1750 g	£7.40	
1751–2000 g	£8.30	
2001–4000 g	£10.30	

Mr Watson wishes to post three packets, one large letter and 12 letters.

The packets weigh 620 g, 1.18 kg and 1.63 kg.

The large letter weighs 425 g.

The letters all weigh less than 100 g.

They will all be sent first class.

Find the total cost of postage.   **(5 marks)**

9. One week Alan works 32 hours from Monday to Friday.

On Saturday he works 6 hours.

From Monday to Friday he is paid £7.20 per hour.

On Saturdays he is paid 25% more per hour.

How much is he paid for the whole week? **(5 marks)**

10. Here are some coins.

Find the smallest amount of money that **cannot** be made with
these coins. **(3 marks)**

11. Gillian wants to catch a plane from Heathrow airport.

The flight departure time is 14 25.

She wants to arrive at the airport at least two hours before the flight
departure time.

She will catch a coach from Chepstow Bus Station to Heathrow airport.

Here is a coach timetable.

Chepstow Bus Station	02 10	04 10	06 10	08 20	10 40	12 40	14 40	16 40
Heathrow Airport	04 45	06 15	08 35	10 45	12 50	14 50	16 50	18 50

She must leave home at least half an hour before the time that the coach
is due to leave.

Find the latest time she can leave home. **(4 marks)**

12. This table shows the prices of single and return train tickets between two cities.

	Single	Return
Standard	£80.75	£100.30
Off-peak (after 9 am)	£27.45	£32.65

Find the difference in price between one off-peak return and two standard singles.

(3 marks)

FOUNDATION AND HIGHER

13. Find the smallest integer that can be written as the sum of two different prime numbers in two different ways.

(3 marks)

14. N is a three-digit number.

The product of the digits of N is 6.

How many different possible values are there for N?

(5 marks)

15. Wallpaper is sold in rolls.

A roll of wallpaper is 53 cm wide and the paper in the roll is 10.05 m long.

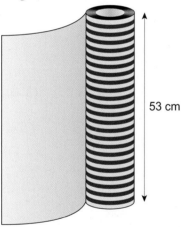

53 cm

James wants to paper a wall.

He has made this sketch.

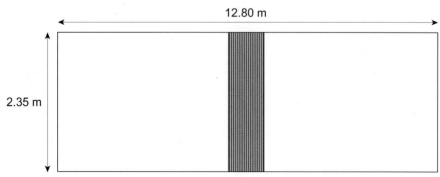

12.80 m

2.35 m

Not drawn accurately

To paper the wall, he will need to cut lengths of wallpaper from a roll.

Each length must be long enough to go from the floor to the ceiling.

They are pasted to the wall edge-to-edge.

What is the smallest number of rolls that James will need? **(4 marks)**

16. Ahmed is 20 years old and Shaki is 50 years old.

    They share some money in the ratio of their ages.

    Shaki gets £600 more than Ahmed.

    How much money is there altogether? **(4 marks)**

17. Yousef takes three tests.

    In test A he scores 28 out of 45.

    In test B he scores 48 out of 70.

    In test C he scored two-thirds of the available marks.

    In which test did he get the best score?

    Give a reason for your answer. **(3 marks)**

18. Find a number between 20 and 30 that is half the sum of its factors. **(3 marks)**

19. Byron is swimming lengths in a pool.

    He has a target of the number of lengths he wants to swim.

    At one point he has swum half his target.

    After six more lengths he has swum three-fifths of his target.

    Work out his target. **(4 marks)**

20. Mel is saving for a holiday.

    She saves the same amount each week.

    After six weeks she has saved 30% of the amount she needs.

    How many **more** weeks will she need to go on saving? **(3 marks)**

21. Mick has a bag of biscuits.

    If he shares them equally among 5 people there will be one biscuit left over.

    If he shares them equally among 7 people there will be one biscuit left over.

    Work out the smallest possible number of biscuits in the bag. **(5 marks)**

22. 8 and 10 can both be written as the sum of two square numbers.

    $8 = 2^2 + 2^2 \qquad 10 = 3^2 + 1^2$

    What is the smallest number that can be written as the sum of two square numbers in two different ways? **(5 marks)**

23. Do not use a calculator for this question.

A and B are two-digit numbers.

$\sqrt{A} \div \sqrt{B} = 3$

Work out the values of A and B.   (4 marks)

24. John is thinking of a three-digit number less than 200.

He halves the number and subtracts 4.

He does the same thing with the answer.

After he has done this several times, the answer is 1.

What is John's number?   (5 marks)

25. A shop is advertising four special offers.

Which is the best value for money?

Give a reason for your answer.   (4 marks)

HIGHER

26. Katie has two square cake tins.

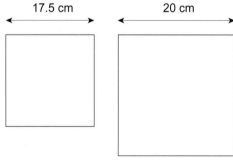

Not drawn accurately

She is baking a cake.

The recipe requires 300 g of flour for a 20 cm square tin.

She will be using a 17.5 cm square tin.

She wants the cake to be the same height as the cake in the recipe.

Work out the amount of flour she needs.   (4 marks)

27. When a ball bounces it rises to 70% of the height it fell from.

The ball is dropped from 2 metres.

How many times will it bounce before it rises less than 50 cm? **(6 marks)**

28. This table gives the distances of the planets from the Sun.

Planet	Mercury	Venus	Earth	Mars
Distance (km)	5.79×10^7	1.08×10^8	1.50×10^8	2.28×10^8

Planet	Jupiter	Saturn	Uranus	Neptune
Distance (km)	7.78×10^8	1.43×10^9	2.87×10^9	4.50×10^9

The distance from The Sun to the Earth is called an astronomical unit (AU).

One day the Sun, Jupiter and Saturn are in a straight line, with Jupiter and Saturn on the same side of the Sun, as shown in the diagram.

Sun   Jupiter   Saturn

Not drawn accurately

Find the distance between Jupiter and Saturn, in astronomical units. **(4 marks)**

29. What is the units digit of the number 3^{30}?

Give a reason for your answer. **(5 marks)**

30. Karla works 40 hours each week and receives an hourly rate of pay.

She gets a pay rise of 10%.

She decides to reduce the number of hours she works each week by 10%.

How will the amount of money she earns each week change? **(6 marks)**

Algebra

FOUNDATION

1. Three times a number is equal to 21 more than the number.

Find the number. (4 marks)

2. Annette bought some oranges and some pineapples.

The oranges cost 20p each and the pineapples cost 75p each.

She paid with a £10 note and received 20p change.

What is the smallest possible number of oranges she bought? (4 marks)

3. The cost (£C) of travelling M miles in a taxi is given by the formula:

$C = 3.5 + 2.5M$

Hattie had to pay £46.00.

How far did she travel? (5 marks)

FOUNDATION AND HIGHER

4. This is the design for a letter C in an alphabet.

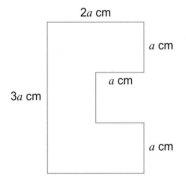

All the angles are right angles.

(a) Find the perimeter, in centimetres.

(b) Find the area, in square centimetres (cm²). (4 marks)

5. Xavier starts counting from 0, going up in 5s.

At the same time, Yusef starts counting from 100, going down in 2s.

They both say one number every two seconds.

Will they ever say the same number at the same time?

Give a reason for your answer. (4 marks)

6. Luna squares her age and adds 1.

Then she squares the answer and adds 2.

The final answer is 10 203.

Find Luna's age. **(4 marks)**

7. John is making a pendulum by tying a mass on the end of a string.

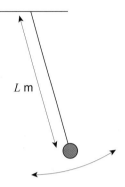

L m

The time *T*, in seconds, for one complete swing of the pendulum is given by the formula:

$$T = 2\pi\sqrt{\frac{L}{9.8}}$$

where *L* is the length of the pendulum, in metres.

John wants the time for one swing to be 1 second so that he can use it as a timer.

Work out the length of the pendulum. **(5 marks)**

8. The equation of line L is $y = 2x + 50$.

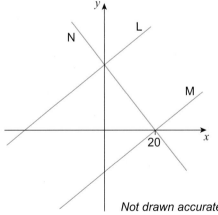

Not drawn accurately

(a) Line M is parallel to line L.

Find the equation of line M.

(b) Find the equation of line N. **(6 marks)**

9. If *N* is a non-negative integer then $(N + 1)^3 - N^3$ is a hexagonal number.

How many two-digit hexagon numbers are there? **(4 marks)**

10. Here is part of a table showing even numbers written in columns.

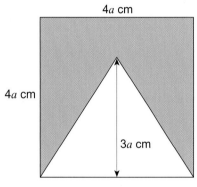

Column

1	2	3	4
2	4	6	8
10	12	14	16
18	20	22	24
26	28	30	
34			

(a) What is the 30th number in column 1?

(b) Show that 500 is in column 2. (6 marks)

11. The diagram shows a square with a triangle inside it.

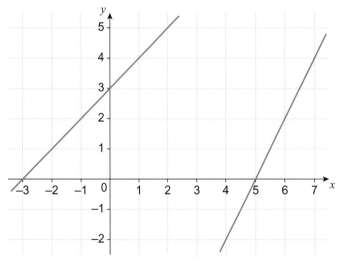

Find the ratio of the area of the shaded part of the square to the area of the unshaded part. (5 marks)

12. If the lines in this diagram are extended they will cross.

Find the coordinates of the point where they cross. (6 marks)

13. Pierre is one quarter of his father's age.

In 16 years' time he will be half his father's age.

How old is Pierre? (6 marks)

14. N is an integer and $N \geqslant 2$.

Prove that $(N + 2)^2 - (N - 2)^2$ is a multiple of 8. (4 marks)

15. In this diagram, the x-axis is a line of symmetry.

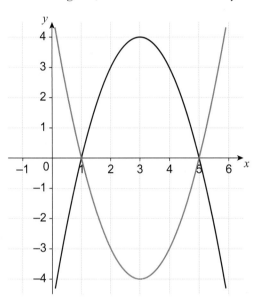

The equation of one curve is $y = x^2 - 6x + 5$.

Find the equation of the other curve. (3 marks)

16. Aaron and Ben have some sweets.

If Aaron gives Ben 10 sweets, they will have the same number of sweets.

If Ben gives Aaron 10 sweets, Aaron will have twice as many as Ben.

How many sweets does each person have? (6 marks)

17. Here is an identity.

$(2x + b)(4x - 3) \equiv ax^2 + 6x - c$

Find the values of a, b and c. (5 marks)

18. Here is a quadratic graph.

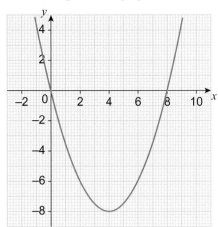

The lowest point on the curve is $(4, -8)$.

Work out the equation of the curve. (4 marks)

19. The ratio of the ages of Jack and Kate is $1 : 2$.

In ten years' time the ratio will be $2 : 3$.

How old are Jack and Kate? (6 marks)

20. p and q are positive numbers.

$p^2 + q^2 = 1108$ and $p^2 - q^2 = 460$

Work out the values of p and q. (4 marks)

21. $x + y = 14$

$x^2 + y^2 = 120$

Prove that $xy = 38$. (4 marks)

22. $\dfrac{N}{N+2} = \dfrac{N+2}{N+5}$

Find the value of N. (4 marks)

23. The golden ratio is a positive number G with the property that the square of G is one more than G.

That is: $G^2 = G + 1$

Find the **exact** value of G. (6 marks)

24. Here is a useful formula.

$$\sin 60° = \frac{\sqrt{3}}{2}$$

The length of each side of an equilateral triangle is a cm.

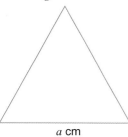

a cm

(a) Show that the area of the triangle is $\frac{\sqrt{3}}{4} a^2$ cm^2.

(b) Find a formula for the area of a regular hexagon of side a cm.

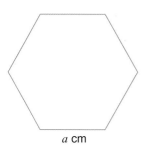

a cm

(4 marks)

25. The nth term of one sequence is $n^2 + 1$.

The nth term of a second sequence is $100 - 2n$.

How many terms appear in **both** sequences? (5 marks)

26. The formula for a person's body mass index (I) is $I = \frac{M}{H^2}$

where M is mass, in kilograms, and H is height, in metres.

Jack's mass is 85 kg. He says, 'My body mass index is less than 25.'

What can you say about his height? (6 marks)

Geometry

1. Here is a rhombus.

The perimeter of the rhombus is 26 cm.

Three rhombuses, identical to the one above, can be put together to make this shape.

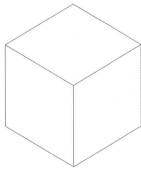

Find the perimeter of this shape.   **(4 marks)**

2. This is a scale drawing of the area in front of a house.

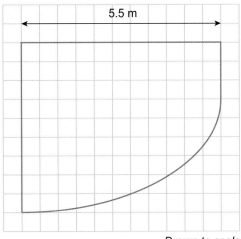

Drawn to scale

The area is being covered with asphalt.

Asphalt costs £15 per square metre.

Estimate the total cost.   **(5 marks)**

3. This rectangle is made from 15 one-centimetre squares joined together.

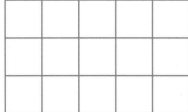

The square in the top right-hand corner is removed.

    (a) Show that the perimeter of the shape has not changed.

    (b) What is the largest number of squares that can be taken away from the rectangle without changing the perimeter?   **(5 marks)**

4. Each time Gavin goes to a football match he keeps the ticket as a souvenir.

The tickets measure 11 cm by 7 cm.

He decides to stick the tickets in a scrapbook.

Each page of the scrapbook measures 24 cm by 34 cm.

The tickets must not overlap.

What is the largest number he can fit on one page?

Give a reason for your answer.   **(5 marks)**

5. Each edge of this cube is 3 cm long.

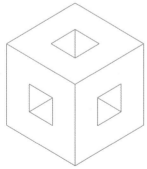

Three square holes are drilled through the cube.

The holes pass through the centre of each face.

The squares holes each have a side length of 1 cm.

Find the volume of the remaining shape.   **(4 marks)**

6. This is a plan of a room.

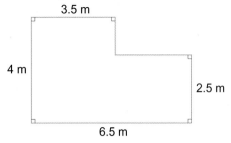

Not drawn accurately

Celia is decorating the room.

She wants to put a decorative strip round the edge of the ceiling.

The strip costs £4.30 per metre.

Find the total cost.

Show how you got your answer.   (5 marks)

7. This diagram is made from two sets of three parallel lines.

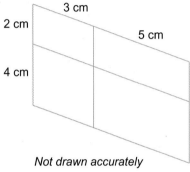

Not drawn accurately

How many parallelograms are there in the diagram?   (3 marks)

8. Eight identical bricks are put together to make a cuboid.

The cuboid is on the ground.

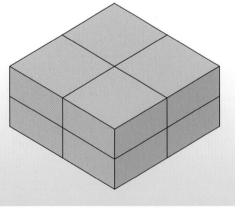

How many faces of the bricks are **not** visible?   (4 marks)

9. The diagram shows a square of side 24 cm.

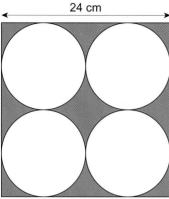

24 cm

There are four circles of equal size inside the square.

Find the area of the shaded region, not covered by the circles. **(5 marks)**

10. The points A and B are 5 m apart.

A   5 m   B

Not drawn accurately

A wheel makes 2 complete rotations in moving from A to B.

Find the radius of the wheel. **(5 marks)**

11. Two rectangular pieces of card both measure 15 cm by 10 cm.

They are placed so that they overlap, as shown.

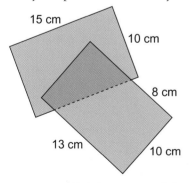

15 cm

10 cm

8 cm

13 cm   10 cm

Not drawn accurately

Find the area of the overlap.

Show your working. **(5 marks)**

12. Here are two shapes.

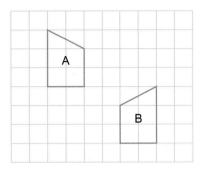

Here are some transformations.

Reflection   Rotation   Translation   Enlargement

(a) Choose **two** of the transformations and explain how they can be used consecutively to map A onto B.

(b) Explain why the other two transformations cannot be used consecutively to map A onto B.

(**4 marks**)

13. Each edge of a cube is 10 cm long.

A vertical cut is made to cut a portion off one corner.

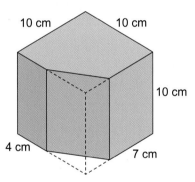

Not drawn accurately

Find the volume of the shape remaining.

(**5 marks**)

14. A regular polygon has N sides.

None of the angles of the polygon is an integer.

Show that the smallest possible value of N is 7.

(**4 marks**)

15. A circular pond has a diameter of 4.6 m.

There is a path all the way round it.

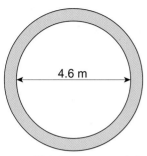

Not drawn accurately

The path is 40 cm wide.

Work out the area of the path.

(5 marks)

16. In the diagram, ABC and BDC are right angles.

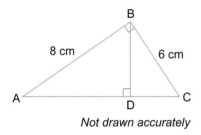

Not drawn accurately

The length of AB is 8 cm and the length of BC is 6 cm.

Calculate BD, the height of the triangle.

(5 marks)

17. **(a)** Show that ABCD is a cyclic quadrilateral.

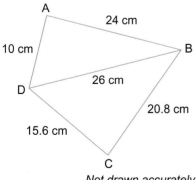

Not drawn accurately

(b) Find the area of ABCD.

(7 marks)

18. A plank, CB, is leaning against a low wall, AX.

The other end of the plank is on the ground.

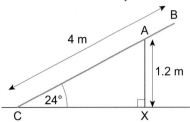

Not drawn accurately

The plank is 4 m long.

The wall is 1.2 m high.

The angle between the plank and the ground is 24°.

Find the length of AB, the amount by which the end of the plank hangs over the wall.

(4 marks)

19. In the diagram, ADE is a tangent to the circle.

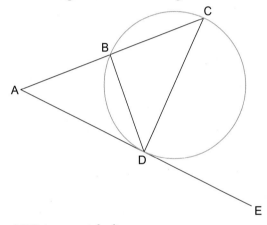

ABC is a straight line.

Show that triangles ABD and ADC are similar.

(4 marks)

20. AB is the cable for an aerial runway.

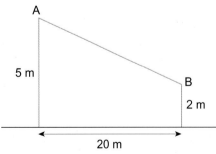

Not drawn accurately

The two ends of the runway are 5 m and 2 m above the ground.

The horizontal distance between them is 20 m.

Find the length of the cable, AB.

(5 marks)

21. In the diagram, OAB is a sector of a circle.

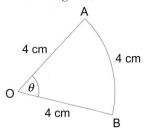

Not drawn accurately

All three sides of the sector are 4 cm long.

(a) Work out the size of the angle labelled θ.

(b) Show that the area of the sector is 8 cm².

(**7 marks**)

22. The inside of a cocktail glass is in the shape of a cone.

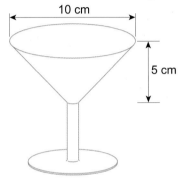

When it is full, the depth of liquid is 5 cm.

Work out the depth when the glass is half full.

(**6 marks**)

Statistics

FOUNDATION

1. Sally and Tamsin play chess every lunchtime.

Here are the results of the last 20 games.

Sally wins	Tamsin wins	Draw
8	4	8

Estimate the probability that Sally will not win the next game.　　　　　　**(3 marks)**

2. In a tombola, tickets are taken out of a drum.

There are winning tickets and losing tickets.

There are 50 winning tickets.

The probability of taking a winning ticket is 0.2.

Find the number of losing tickets.　　　　　　**(3 marks)**

3. Here are the ages of five people

Name	Amber	Belle	Camilla	Daisy	Elfine	Fiona
Age (years)	33	24	29	31	32	47

Whose age is closest to the mean?　　　　　　**(4 marks)**

4. Two dice are rolled.

Find the probability that the number on one is double the number on the other.　　　　　　**(4 marks)**

5. A survey finds the mass and height of several hundred children.

The masses vary from 20 kg to 50 kg.

The heights vary from 1.10 m to 1.60 m.

Design a two-way table to record the grouped frequencies.　　　　　　**(4 marks)**

FOUNDATION AND HIGHER

6. There is a lottery draw every week.

The probability of winning a £10 prize is 0.08.

(a) One week 5000 people buy a lottery ticket.

Estimate how many will win £10.

(b) One week 7200 people won £10.

Estimate how many people bought a ticket.　　　　　　**(5 marks)**

7. Here are the results of a survey of the masses of some pet dogs.

	Frequency
Healthy	110
Overweight	50
Obese	20
Underweight	60
Total	240

Illustrate these results in a pie chart. (6 marks)

8. A group of women take part in an experiment.

Each throws one dice until she gets an even number.

Each counts the number of throws she makes.

The results are shown in this frequency table.

Throws	1	2	3	4	5	6	7	8
Frequency	38	18	6	5	2	0	1	2

(a) Find the total number of throws.

(b) Which average is the largest, the mode, the median or the mean number of throws?

Give a reason for your answer. (5 marks)

9. Here are four lengths.

38 cm   49 cm   53 cm   72 cm

Show that one length is the mean of the other three. (4 marks)

10. Boys and girls are tested to see how long they take to complete a simple task.

Here are their times, in seconds.

```
Boys                          Girls

2 |  3 8 9 9              2 |  6 7 7 8 9
3 |  0 2 4 6 8            3 |  1 1 2 2 2 4 6
4 |  1 1 1 1 4 5 7        4 |  0 3 5 7
5 |  2 3 3 8              5 |  3 6
6 |  4 9                  6 |  5
```

Key: 2 | 8   means 28

Calculate appropriate statistics and use them to compare the times of boys and girls. (7 marks)

11. Four numbers have a mode of 100, a median of 101 and a mean of 102.

What is the range? (5 marks)

12. Angus works in a telephone call centre.

In the morning he answers 60 calls.

The mean length of a morning call is 3 minutes and 40 seconds.

In the afternoon he answers 40 calls.

The mean length of an afternoon call is 4 minutes and 20 seconds.

What is the mean length of all 100 calls? **(5 marks)**

13. An investigation of the weather records for a town gives these results.

The probability of 5 or more rainy days in April is 0.45.

The probability of 5 or fewer rainy days in April is 0.75.

What is the probability of 5 rainy days in April?

Show your working. **(3 marks)**

HIGHER

14. Here is some information about the ages (in years) of the employees in two factories.

Factory	Number of people	Mean age	Median age	Oldest person	Youngest person	Interquartile range	Percentage under 30
A	786	32.2	29	66	16	14	51.1%
B	1241	37.1	34	64	17	20	40.6%

Use the information given to compare the ages of the workers in the two factories. **(5 marks)**

15. Here are the test marks for 12 students in three subjects.

Student	A	B	C	D	E	F	G	H	I	J	K	L
Economics	20	22	25	28	32	36	39	40	40	42	45	47
Latin	20	34	15	35	25	25	32	27	22	30	28	17
Sociology	29	21	35	15	30	40	25	20	39	20	35	44

Investigate whether there is any correlation between the marks for different subjects. **(4 marks)**

16. Monty drives through two sets of traffic lights every day on his way to work.

The probability that he has to stop at the first set is 0.75.

The probability that he has to stop at the second set is 0.6.

The two sets of lights operate independently.

(a) What is the probability that he has to stop at both sets of lights on his way to work on Monday?

(b) What is the probability that he has to stop at both sets of lights on his way to work on Monday and on Tuesday? **(4 marks)**

17. Alan, Brian and Claudine are discussing their ages.

Alan says, 'The mean age of Brian and Claudine is 19.'

Brian says, 'The mean age of Alan and Claudine is 15.'

Claudine says, 'The mean age of Alan and Brian is 14.'

Find the mean age of all three people.

(5 marks)

18. These cumulative frequency curves show the heights of some boys and girls.

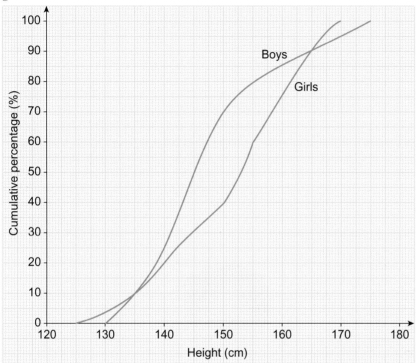

Compare the heights of the boys and the girls.

Calculate appropriate statistics to do this.

(7 marks)

19. This box plot shows the distribution of the lengths of a sample of fish.

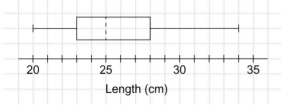

Show this information on a cumulative percentage curve.

(5 marks)

20. This histogram shows the times a group of people took to get to work.

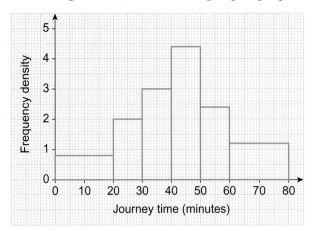

What percentage took less than 30 minutes to get to work? **(5 marks)**

21. This table shows the heights of 1260 teenagers, recorded to the nearest centimetre.

Height (m)	1.50–1.54	1.55–1.59	1.60–1.64	1.65–1.69	1.70–1.74	1.75–1.79
Frequency	157	151	352	332	176	92

4.7% of the teenagers are more than 1.76 m tall.

The interquartile range of the teenagers' heights is 12.8 cm.

Show that one of these statements **could** be true but the other one **must** be false. **(6 marks)**

Mixed questions

1. This is part of the net of a cube.

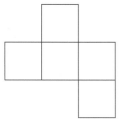

One face is missing from the net.

Show all the places where the missing face could be added.   **(3 marks)**

2. These are the prices of seats at a theatre.

	Monday to Thursday	**Friday and Saturday**
Full price	£16.50	£22.50
Concessions (children and senior citizens)	£11.75	£16.75

A family is going to the theatre.

There are:

- two adults, who will pay full price
- a grandmother, who is a senior citizen
- three children.

They are going on Wednesday.

Calculate the price of the tickets.   **(3 marks)**

3. An airline keeps a record of luggage temporarily lost on its flights.

They produce the following probabilities.

Luggage lost for:	**Probability**
up to 24 hours	0.004
24 to 48 hours	0.0015
more than 48 hours	0.0008

In March, 65 000 people are booked to fly with the airline.

Use the information in the table to estimate the number of people that will lose their luggage in March.   **(3 marks)**

4. The **product** of two integers is −16.

Find all the possible values of the **sum** of the two integers. (**3 marks**)

5. Fence panels are 2 metres long.

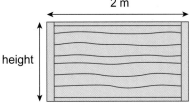

They are available in different heights.

Here are the costs.

Height of panel (m)	1.2	1.5	1.8	2.1
Cost (£)	21.45	27.45	30.95	33.25

Delivery charge: 10% of total order

Matt wants a fence 16 m long.

It will be 1.5 m high.

The panels will be delivered.

Work out the total cost. (**5 marks**)

6. The bar chart shows the numbers of students absent each day of the week.

They are all in the same year group.

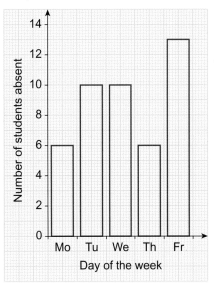

(**a**) Find the mean number of students absent each day.

(**b**) There are 160 students in the year group.

The target for the school is to have less than 7% absent on each day.

On how many days did the school meet its target?

Give a reason for your answer (**5 marks**)

7. This pie chart shows the grades achieved by all the candidates in one school in a GCSE examination.

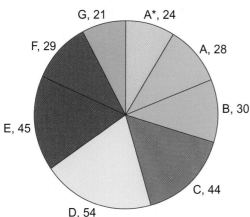

Students gaining each grade

G, 21   A*, 24

F, 29   A, 28

E, 45   B, 30

C, 44

D, 54

What proportion of those who gained A*–C were awarded an A*?   **(3 marks)**

8. These are the prices of some items in a sale.

Item	Original price	Sale price
Formal shirt	£70.00	£22.95
Casual shirt	£80.00	£22.95
Polo shirt	£56.00	£22.95
Handmade tie	£90.00	£29.50

Harry buys a formal shirt, a casual shirt and two ties.

Calculate his percentage saving, based on the original prices.   **(4 marks)**

9. The cost of electricity is in two parts.

Each unit used costs 13.38p.

There is a standing charge of 14p per day.

The number of units used is the difference between two meter readings.

At the start of a 93-day period the meter reading is 25 643.

At the end of that period the meter reading is 26 178.

Calculate the cost of the electricity used in that 93-day period.   **(4 marks)**

10. Here are five number cards.

Irene arranges the cards to make a multiplication of a 3-digit number by a 2-digit number.

Find the largest possible answer. **(3 marks)**

11. The graph shows the stopping distances, in metres, for a car driving on a dry, level road at different speeds.

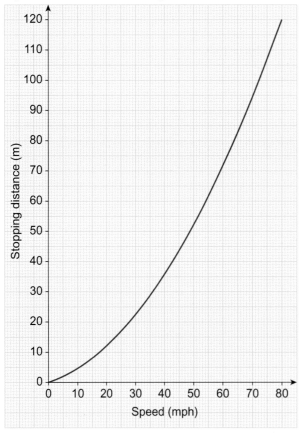

Car A and Car B are travelling on a motorway.

Car A is travelling at 70 mph.

The stopping distance for car B is two-thirds of the stopping distance for car A.

Find the speed of car B. **(3 marks)**

12. On a farm there are goats, sheep and chickens.

The ratio of goats to sheep is 2 : 3.

The ratio of sheep to chickens is 2 : 5.

What is the ratio of goats to chickens? (**3 marks**)

13. Here are the first four patterns in a sequence.

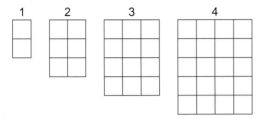

There are two squares in pattern number 1 and six squares in pattern number 2.

Explain how you could work out the number of squares in any pattern. (**3 marks**)

14. Two fractions add up to 1.

The difference between them is $\frac{3}{4}$.

What are the fractions? (**3 marks**)

15. This shape is cut from a square of card.

All the angles are right angles.

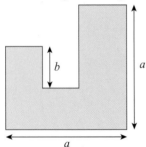

Find an expression for the perimeter of the shape, in terms of a and b. (**3 marks**)

16. **Exactly** 80% of the houses in a street have a front lawn.

Exactly 75% of the houses in the street have a car on the drive.

What is the smallest possible number of houses in the street? (**3 marks**)

17. Jodi and Karl each throw a dice.

Find the probability that Jodi throws a higher number than Karl. (**3 marks**)

18. You can buy euros **from** a bank or sell them **to** the bank.

If you buy them from the bank you can get €1.09 for £1.00.

If you sell them to the bank you can get £1.00 for €1.23.

How much will you lose if you buy €100 from the bank and then sell them back?

Give your answer in pounds. **(3 marks)**

19. Jasmine is thinking of a two-digit number.

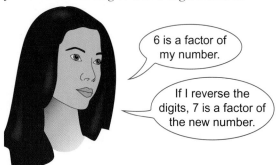

6 is a factor of my number.

If I reverse the digits, 7 is a factor of the new number.

What are the possible values of Jasmine's number? **(4 marks)**

20. If N is a positive integer then $\dfrac{N(N+1)}{2}$ is called a triangular number.

How many three-digit triangular numbers are there? **(4 marks)**

21. Arthur is using loft boards to put a floor in his loft.

Loft boards are rectangular panels 69 cm long and 32 cm wide.

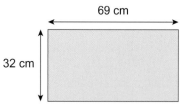

The floor is rectangular and measures 3 m by 4 m.

Arthur can cut the boards if necessary.

He has 50 loft boards. Is this enough?

Give a reason for your answer. **(4 marks)**

22. All the employees in a firm are given the same percentage pay rise.

Alan's monthly salary increases from £2450.00 to £2508.80.

Betty's monthly salary before the increase is £3055.00.

What is Betty's monthly salary after the pay rise? **(3 marks)**

23. Adam draws rectangles that all have the same perimeter.

He finds the width and the area of each rectangle.

He draws this graph to show his results.

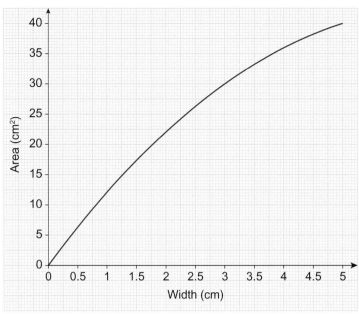

Find the perimeter of each of the rectangles that Adam drew. (4 marks)

24. There are 60 cows in a field. Some are brown and the rest are white.

Two-thirds of the brown cows are less than one year old.

Three-quarters of the white cows are less than one year old.

There are 12 more brown cows than white cows.

What fraction of all the cows are less than one year old? (5 marks)

25. Two cars are on a motorway travelling at 100 km per hour (63 miles per hour).

Attention all drivers!

STAY SAFE!

Follow the two-second rule

Stay at least 2 seconds

behind the car in front of you

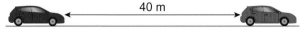

The cars are 40 metres apart.

Use the two-second rule to decide whether this is a safe distance.

Give a reason for your answer. (4 marks)

26. Here are two cylindrical cans of food.

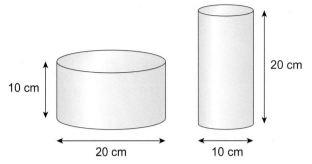

10 cm

20 cm

20 cm

10 cm

Compare the volumes of the two cans. (5 marks)

27. The total of Roger's age and Saleem's age is 61.

The total of Saleem's age and Teri's age is 89.

The total of Teri's age and Roger's age is 76.

Find the total of Roger's age, Saleem's age and Teri's age. (3 marks)

28. Mick has lasagne, a banana and a can of cola for lunch.

On a website he finds this information about the number of calories in what he has eaten.

Item	Quantity	Calories
Lasagne	1 serving/400 g	588
Banana	Medium/150 g	144
Cola	1 can/330 g	142

He estimates that he had 500 g of lasagne and a large banana with a mass of 200 g.

Find the number of calories in Mick's lunch. (4 marks)

29. Here are three cards.

Each card has a positive whole number written on the back.

The number on card X is a multiple of 3.

The number on card Y is a multiple of 5.

The number on card Z is a multiple of 7.

The three numbers add up to 100.

What is the largest possible number that could be on card X? (4 marks)

30. Three identical rectangular cards are arranged so that they overlap.

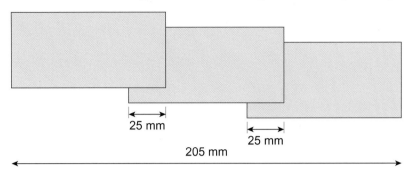

The overlaps are 25 mm.

The total length is 205 mm.

Find the length of each card. **(4 marks)**

31. The area of a circle is A cm^2.

The circumference of a circle is C cm.

Show that:

$A = \dfrac{C^2}{4\pi}$ **(4 marks)**

32. A circle passes through the vertices of an equilateral triangle.

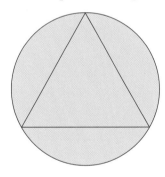

The perimeter of the triangle is 30 cm.

Calculate the circumference of the circle. **(5 marks)**

33. Radio signals travel at 3.00×10^8 m/s.

The distance from the Earth to the Moon is 239 000 km.

How long does it take for a radio signal to travel from the Earth to the Moon? **(3 marks)**

34. This is a hemisphere (half a sphere) with a diameter of d cm.

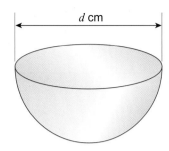

d cm

The volume, V cm^3, of a hemisphere with a diameter of d cm is given by the formula:

$$v = \frac{\pi d^3}{12}$$

Work out the diameter of a hemisphere with a volume of 500 cm^3.

(3 marks)

35. Three points, A, B and C, are in a straight line on level ground.

There is a tree at B and a tree at C.

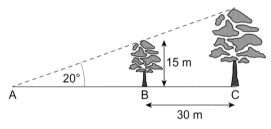

20°

15 m

A   B   C

30 m

Not drawn accurately

The trees are 30 m apart.

The tree at B is 15 m high.

The angle of elevation of both trees from A is 20°.

Calculate the height of the tree at C.

(5 marks)

36. Ali and Briony are playing a game.

Each one starts with 0 points. They throw a dice in turn.

A six **adds** a certain number of points to the thrower's total.

A one **subtracts** a different number of points from the thrower's total.

There is no change if any other number is scored.

Here are the frequencies for each number, after each of them has thrown the dice 20 times.

	Six	One	Other numbers	Total points
Ali	2	4	14	2
Briony	3	3	14	9

How many points do they get for a six?

(4 marks)

37. The diagram shows two congruent regular 12-sided polygons joined at one edge.

A, B and C are vertices.

B and C are joined with a straight line.

Prove that ABC is an equilateral triangle.

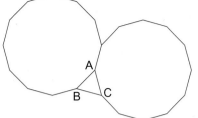

(5 marks)

38. The diameter of a square is d cm.

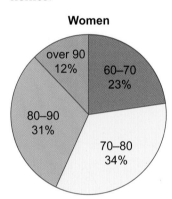

Show that the area of the square is $\frac{1}{2}d^2$ cm^2.

(3 marks)

39. The pie charts show the ages of men and women in a group of residential homes.

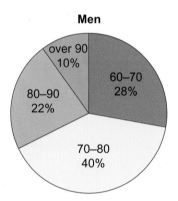

The ratio of women to men is 5 : 3.

There are 30 women in the over-90 class.

How many men are there in the over-90 class?

(5 marks)

40. In the diagram, BC is 10 cm long.

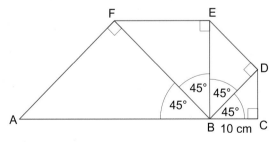

Find the length of AB.

(4 marks)

Formula sheet

Area of trapezium = $\frac{1}{2}(a + b)h$

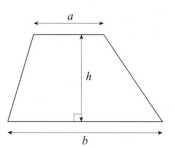

Volume of prism = area of cross-section × length

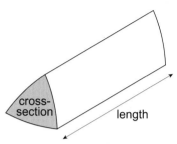

Volume of sphere = $\frac{4}{3}\pi r^3$

Surface area of a sphere = $4\pi r^2$

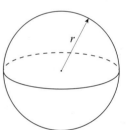

Volume of a cone = $\frac{1}{3}\pi r^2 h$

Curved surface area of a cone = $\pi r l$

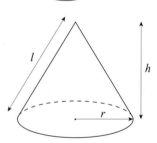

In any triangle ABC:

- area of the triangle = $\frac{1}{2}ab \sin C$

- sine rule $\dfrac{a}{\sin A} = \dfrac{a}{\sin B} = \dfrac{a}{\sin C}$

- cosine rule $a^2 = b^2 + c^2 - 2bc \cos A$

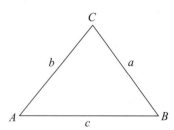

The quadratic equation

The solutions of the general quadratic equation $ax^2 + bx + c = 0$ are given by:

$$x = \frac{-b \pm \sqrt{b^2 - 4ac}}{2a}$$

Answers

Abbreviations used

M	Method marks awarded for a correct method.
A	Accuracy marks awarded when following from a correct method. In some cases it is not necessary to see the method and it can be implied.
B	Marks awarded independent of any method.
FT	Follow-through marks, awarded for correct working following an earlier error.
OE	Or an equivalent.
QWC	Quality of written communication is being assessed. See the explanation in the introductory section.

Number answers

Q	Answer	Marks	Comments
1	Quantities must be multiplied by 2.5 or any statement that implies this. Almonds = 125 g Butter = 125 g Flour = 7 or 7.5 or 8 tbsp Sugar = 250 g Cream = 5 tbsp Vanilla = 2.5 tsp	M1 M1 A2	Allow any valid method that identifies correct proportions. Method mark for applying any valid method correctly, for example, × 2.5 or ÷ 2 then × 5. Lose A1 for each numerical error. Lose a maximum of A1 for lack of or incorrect units.
2	12.50 + 5.25 + 1.85 + 1.50 + 3.89 = (£)24.99	M1 M1 A1	Do not penalise for lack of £ sign.
3	24 40 12 60	B4	1 mark for each.
4	The first digit must be 5 or 6. Tests 6367 and 5763 5763	M1 M1 A1	Recognition that the first digit is 5 or 6. Award all 3 marks if the correct number is given.
5	$19.95 \times 5 = 99.75$ $31.50 \times 2 = 63.00$ 99.75 + 63.00 = (£)162.75	M1A1 M1A1 A1	FT
6	Three distances to add: 58 + 45 + 64 = 167 (miles)	M1 A1 A1	Condone lack of units.
7	4×24.50 $+ 3 \times 11.75$ $+ 4 \times 4.95$ + 3.25 = (£)156.30	M1 M1 M1 A1	FT

8	2.70 + 5.60 + 7.40	M1A1	M for using first-class prices.
	1.60 + 12 × 0.60	M1A1	
	(£)24.50	A1	
9	7.20 × 32 = 230.40	M1	M1 for any valid method of finding 25%.
	7.20 + 25% = 9.00	M1A1	
	9.00 × 6 = 54.00	M1	
	230.40 + 54.00 = (£)284.40	A1	
10	Systematic approach, for example, working up from 1p.	M1	
	Any comment to make searching more efficient, for example, any amount from 1p to 9p is possible, so go up in 10s.	M1	
	41p	A1	Award all 3 marks if the answer is given.
11	Must arrive by 12 25 ⇒ 10 40 coach is too late, 08 20 coach from Chepstow is the latest.	M1 A1	
	30 minutes earlier is 07 50.	M1	
	Latest time is 07 50.	A1	
12	80.75 × 2	M1	
	− 32.65	M1	
	= (£)128.85	A1	
13	Only need to look at even numbers.	M1	
	Work systematically, try 2, 4, etc.	M1	
	16	A1	
14	Identify possible sets of three digits as 1, 2, 3 and 1, 1, 6.	M1 A1	M1A0 for finding only one set.
	Find six ways to arrange 1, 2, 3.	M1	
	Find three ways to arrange 1, 1, 6.	M1	
	Answer: 9	A1	
15	10.05 ÷ 2.35 ⇒ 4 drops per roll	M1	Round down for M1.
	12.8 ÷ 0.53 ⇒ 25 drops	M1	Round up for M1.
	25 ÷ 4 ⇒ 7 rolls	M1	Round up for M1.
	7	A1	
	Or		
	10.05 ÷ 2.35 ⇒ 4 drops per roll	M1	Round down.
	One roll = 4 × 0.53 = 2.12 m	M1	
	12.8 ÷ 2.12 = 7 rolls	M1	Round up.
	7	A1	

16	Ratio 2 : 5	M1	Simplify the ratio.
	£600 is 3 parts $\Rightarrow$ £200 is 1 part.	M1	M1 for identifying what portion the difference is.
	$7 \times 200 = £1400$	M1A1	
	Or		
	Ratio = 2 : 5	M1	
	$\frac{3}{7} = £600$	M1	
	Whole $= \frac{7}{3} \times 600 = 1400$	M1A1	
17	A: $\frac{28}{45} \times 100 = 62.2...\%$	M1	M1 for any appropriate method.
	B: $\frac{50}{70} \times 100 = 71.4...\%$	A1	
	C: $\frac{2}{3} = 66.6...\%$		
	B is best, with the highest percentage.	A1	Allow FT. Reason must be stated to gain the mark.
18	Find factors of some values.	M1	Efficient method, for example, cannot be a prime number; realises some numbers are more likely than others.
	Cannot be prime.	M1	
	28	A1	
19	$\frac{3}{5}$ of target $- \frac{1}{2}$ of target $= 6$	M1	Attempt to find difference between fractions.
	$\frac{3}{5} - \frac{1}{2} = \frac{1}{10}$	M1A1	Valid method for subtraction.
	Target $= 10 \times 6 = 60$	A1	
20	Use proportion, any valid method, for example:	M2	M1 for identifying 30% and 6 weeks and indicating that 100% is needed.
	$30\% = 6$ weeks $\Rightarrow 100\% = 6 \div 0.3 = 20$		
	$20 - 6 = 14$ weeks	A1	M1 for attempting any valid method.
	Or		
	$30\% = 6$ weeks $\Rightarrow 10\% = 2$ weeks $\Rightarrow$ $100\% = 20$ weeks $\Rightarrow 14$ weeks more		
21	Multiple of 5 plus 1 is 6, 11, 16, ... or 'ends in 1 or 6'.	M1A1	
	Multiple of 7 plus 1 = 8, 15, 22, ...	M1A1	
	Answer: 36	A1	
	Or		
	Answer will be 1 more that the LCM of 5 and 7.	M1A1	
	LCM is 35.	M1A1	
	Answer is 36.	A1	
22	List of squares.	M1	List of squares seen.
	Systematic method, for example, listing sums in order or putting sums in a table.	M1A1	A1 for adding squares correctly.
	50	A2	A1 if just one of $7^2 + 1^2$ and $5^2 + 5^2$ is seen.

23	$\sqrt{A} = 3\sqrt{B}$ $A = 9B$ $A = 99$ and $B = 11$	M1A1 M1A1	M1 for an attempt to find a relationship between A and B by any method. These are the only possible values. No marks if a calculator is used.
24	Use inverse operations. $(1 + 4) \times 2 = 10$ $(10 + 4) \times 2 = 28$ $(28 + 4) \times 2 = 64$ $(64 + 4) \times 2 = 136$ $(136 + 4) \times 2 = 280$, which is more than 200. Answer: 136	M1 A1 A1 M1 A1	A1 for three correct iterations. M1 for showing that there is only one solution.
25	Find the reduction for each. $\frac{1}{3}, \frac{1}{4}, \frac{1}{4}, \frac{1}{4}$ **Or** Choose an arbitrary price and find the new price for each offer. **Or** Find the percentage paid: $66\frac{2}{3}$, 75, 75, 75. **Or** Any other valid method of comparing. Three for the price of two.	M1A1 A2 QWC	A1 for correct answer. A1 for clear explanation.
26	Quantity is proportional to the area of the base. **Either** $17.5^2 \div 20^2 = 0.76\ldots$ $300 \times 0.76 \ldots$ **Or** Any other valid method, for example, $300 \div 20^2 \times 17.5^2$. Answer: Any whole number of grams from 225 to 230 inclusive.	M1 A1 M1 A1	A0 for a decimal answer.
27	First bounce is to 1.4 m. Second bounce is to 0.98 m. Third bounce is to 0.686 m. Fourth bounce is to 0.4802 m. Four	M1A1 M1A1 M1 A1	Any method, for example, 0.7×2. Finding percentage of new height. Repeating the process.
28	Distance in km is 6.52×10^8. Distance in AU is 4.3(466…) **Or** Convert distances to AU before subtraction: $9.53 - 5.19$ AU.	M1A1 M1A1	$1.43 \times 10^9 - 7.78 \times 10^8$ $6.52 \div 1.50$

29	Units digits of successive powers of 3 are 3, 9, 7, 1, 3, …	M1A1	
	This repeats every four terms.	A1	
	30th term is 9 because $30 \div 4$ has a remainder of 2.	M1	
	Answer: 9	A1 QWC	M0 if no justification is seen.
30	New pay = old pay $\times$ 1.1	M1A1	Calculating increase.
	$\times$ 0.9	M1A1	Calculating decrease.
	= old pay $\times$ 0.99	M1	Overall result.
	1% reduction	A1	Should be given as a percentage.
	Or		
	Student chooses a specific value for the rate of pay and does a numerical calculation.		Award marks in a similar way. Change must be given as a percentage.

Algebra answers

Q	Answer	Marks	Comments
1	$3x = x + 21$	M1A1	M1 for attempting to form an equation. It could be in words or use a different symbol.
	$x = 10.5$	M1A1	M1 for an attempt to solve the equation.
2	Total cost is 980p.	M1	M1 for looking for a combination that gives 980.
	$12 \times 75p = 900$	M1	M1 for looking for the maximum number of pineapples.
	12 is the maximum number of pineapples.	A1	
	4 is the minimum number of oranges.	A1	
3	$46 = 3.5 + 2.5M$	M1A1	Form an equation.
	$M = 17$	M1A1	Solve the equation by any method.
	17 miles	A1	'Miles' must be seen for the accuracy mark.
4a	$12a$	M1A1	M1 for evidence of a valid method for finding the perimeter.
4b	$5a^2$	M1A1	M1 for any valid method. This could involve dividing into rectangles or subtracting a square from the large rectangle.
5	Only multiples of 10 can be in both lists.	M1	Only need to record 10-second intervals but no penalty for doing more.
	100 (0), 90 (25), 80 (50), 70 (75)	M1	
	No. The sequence above shows this.	A2 QWC	A1 if the explanation is partial or unconvincing.

6	Use inverse operations.	M1	M1 for an attempt to use inverse operations.
	$\sqrt{10\,203 - 2} = 101$	A1	
	$\sqrt{101 - 1} = 10$	M1A1	
7	$1 = 2\pi\sqrt{\dfrac{l}{9.8}}$	M1	Substitute to give an equation.
	$0.159 = \sqrt{\dfrac{l}{9.8}}$	M1	Rearrange.
	$l = 0.159^2 \times 9.8$	M1	Square to eliminate square root sign.
	$= 0.24(775\ldots)$	A1	
	0.25 m or 25 cm	A1	Round answer sensibly and include units to get the mark.
8a	$y = 2x - 40$	A1	2 is coefficient of x.
		M1A1	M1 for using the gradient to find the intercept on the y-axis.
			A1 for -40
8b	$y = -2.5x + 50$	M1A1	Finding that the gradient is -2.5.
		A1	For 50.
9	$N = 2$ gives 19.	M1	Substituting value systematically.
	$N = 3$ gives 37.		
	$N = 4$ gives 61.		
	$N = 5$ gives 91.	A1	Trying all possible values.
	These are the only two-digit values.	A1	
	Answer: 4	A1	
10a	Numbers increase by 8.	A1	
	$2 + 29 \times 8 = 234$	M1A1	Allow any equivalent method such as $30 \times 8 - 4$.
10b	$500 \div 8$ has remainder 4.	M1A1	M1 for identifying the remainder as the deciding number.
	Remainders for columns 1, 2, 3 and 4 are 2, 4, 6 and 0 respectively.		
	500 must be in column 2.	A1 QWC	
	Or		
	Numbers in column 4 go up in 8s.		Award marks for any valid method. A clear explanation is required for full marks.
	$500 - 4 = 496 = 62 \times 8 =$ a multiple of 8.		
	500 must be in column 2.		
11	Area of square is $16a^2$.	A1	This is $4a \times 4a$.
	Area of triangle is $6a^2$.	M1A1	This is $\frac{1}{2} \times 4a \times 3a$.
	Area unshaded is $10a^2$.		
	$10 : 6 = 5 : 3$	M1A1	Simplify the ratio to get both marks.
12	$y = x + 3$	A1	
	$y = 2x - 10$	M1A1	Method for finding equation seen.
	Solve $2x - 10 = x + 3$.	M1	
	Point of intersection is $(13, 16)$.	A2	A1 for each coordinate.

13	$p = \frac{1}{4}f$	A1	
	$p + 16 = \frac{1}{2}(f + 16)$	M1 A1	
	Either		
	$\frac{1}{4}f + 16 = \frac{1}{2}f + 8$	M1	Eliminate one variable.
	$8 = \frac{1}{4}f$	M1	Rearrange to solve.
	Father's age is 32,	A1	Father's age is not required.
	Pierre's age is 8.		Pierre's age.
	Or		Any valid method will be awarded the marks.
	Any other method of solving the equations.		
14	Attempt to simplify.	M1	
	Either		
	$N^2 + 4N + 4 - (N^2 - 4N + 8) = 8N$	M1A1	Multiply out and simplify
	Or		or
	$(N + 2 + N - 2)(N + 2 - [N - 2]) = 8N$		use the difference of two squares.
	$8N$ is a multiple of N because N is an integer.	A1 QWC	
15	y-coordinate has the opposite sign.	M1	
	$y = -(x^2 - 6x + 5)$	A1	
	$y = -x^2 + 6x - 5$	A1	
16	$a - 10 = b + 10$	M1A1	Form two correct equations.
	$a + 10 = 2(b - 10)$		
	Eliminate one variable, for example:	M1	
	$20 = b - 30$		
	Solve the equation to find one variable:		
	$b = 50$		
	Ben has 50 sweets.	A1	
	Substitute to form an equation for the other variable, for example:	M1	
	$a - 10 = 60$		
	Solve:		
	$a = 70$		Allow any other valid method and allocate marks accordingly.
	Aaron has 70 sweets.	A1	
17	$8x^2 + (4b - 6)x - 3b \equiv ax^2 + 6x - c$	M2	Multiply out brackets and equate coefficients to form three equations.
	$8 = a$	A1	
	$4b - 6 = 6$		
	$3b = c$		
	$b = 3$ and $c = 9$	A2	FT from an incorrect b to find c.

18	Form of equation is $y = ax(x - 8)$.	M1A1	Use the points where the graph crosses the x-axis to find an equation.
	$-8 = a \times 4 \times -4$ $a = \dfrac{1}{2}$ or 0.5	M1	Substitute to find the value of a.
	$y = 0.5x(x - 8)$	A1	Allow any other method, for example, writing $y = ax^2 + bx$ and finding the values of a and b.
19	$k = 2j$ $k + 10 = \dfrac{3}{2}(j + 10)$	M1A1	Form two equations.
	Eliminate one variable, for example: $2j + 10 = 1.5j + 15$	M1	
	Solve to find one variable, for example: $j = 10$	A1	
	Substitute to find the other, for example: $k = 20$	M1	
	Jack is 10 and Kate is 20.	A1	Award marks for any method.
20	$2p^2 = 1108 + 460 = 1568$ $p^2 = 784$	M1	Eliminate one variable.
	$p = 28$	A1	Find the square root. Only the positive root is required since p is positive.
	$2q^2 = 1108 - 460 = 648$ $q^2 = 324$	M1	Use any method to find the other variable.
	$q = 18$	A1	
21	$(x + y)^2 = x^2 + 2xy + y^2$ $= 14^2 = 196$	M1A1	
	$2xy = 196 - 120$	M1	The algebra must be written correctly to get full marks.
	$xy = 38$	A1 QWC	Award appropriate marks for any valid method. For full marks the algebra must be correct.
			Note that it is not necessary to find the values of x and y.
22	$N(N + 5) = (N + 2)^2$ $N^2 + 5N = N^2 + 4N + 4$	M1	Eliminating the fractions by multiplication.
	$5N = 4N + 4$	M1A1	
	$N = 4$	A1	
23	$G^2 - G - 1 = 0$	M1A1	Rearrange to get 0 on one side.
	Use the quadratic formula.	M1	
	The positive root is $G = \dfrac{\sqrt{5} + 1}{2}$	M1A2 QWC	M1 for taking the positive root and simplifying. A1 if the simplification is incomplete.
			For full marks the answer must be in surd form, not a decimal approximation.

24a	Area $= \frac{1}{2} ab \sin C = \frac{1}{2} \times a \times a \times \frac{\sqrt{3}}{2}$ $= \frac{\sqrt{3}}{4} a^2$ **Or** use $\frac{1}{2}$ base $\times$ height.	M1A1 QWC	
24b	Hexagon = 6 triangles Area $= 6 \times \frac{\sqrt{3}}{4} a^2 = 1.5\sqrt{3}a^2$	M1A1	Allow any equivalent formula but A0 if $\sqrt{3}$ is replaced by a decimal approximation.
25	First sequence is 2, 5, 10, ….	A1	A1
	Second sequence is 98, 96, 94, ….	A1	A1
	Common terms are even numbers less than 100 that are 1 more than a square number.	M1	M1
	So 'odd square + 1': 2, 10, 26, 50, 82	A1	A1
	There are five terms.	A1	A1
26	$\frac{85}{H^2} < 25$	M1A1	
	$H^2 > \frac{85}{25}$	M1A1	
	$H > \sqrt{3.4}$	M1	
	Height is greater than 1.84 m (or 1.844 m).	A1 QWC	Must give units and round to 2 or 3 d.p.

Geometry answers

Q	Answer	Marks	Comments
1	One edge is 6.5 cm or two edges are 13 cm.	M1A1	
	6×6.5 cm or 13 cm $\times$ 3 = 39 cm	M1A1	
2	1 square = 0.25 m^2 or 4 squares = 1 m^2.	M1	
	Area is 85 ± 2 squares or equivalent.	A1	Counting squares.
	Area is 21 to 22 m^2	A1	
	Total cost is £315 to £330.	M1A1	FT from an incorrect area if method is clear.
3a	Any indication that the perimeter of each shape is 16 cm.	M1A1	Explanation could include labelling a diagram. Perimeter does not need to be stated as 16 if equality is indicated.
3b	8	M2A1	M1 for removing squares while keeping perimeter the same. M1 for a systematic approach.
4	Nine can be arranged in three rows of three.	A1	
	Three 11 cm lengths will fit in 34 cm because $3 \times 11 = 33$.		
	Three 7 cm lengths will fit in 24 cm because $3 \times 7 = 21$.	M1A1	This could be shown in a diagram with lengths indicated.
	Arranging the tickets the other way round, only 2 rows of 4 are possible.	M1A1 QWC	Must indicate that the other possibility is not as good.

5	20 cm^3	M2A2	M1 for attempting to find the volume removed or the volume remaining directly. M1 for a systematic approach to doing this, for example, remove $3 + 2 + 2$ centimetre cubes or $8 + 8 + 4$ centimetre cubes remain. A1 for partially correct calculation.
6	Perimeter = 21 m Cost = £4.30 × 21 = £90.30	M2A1 M1A1 QWC	M1 for attempt to find perimeter. M1 for attempt to find missing lengths. The calculation must be shown to get full marks.
7	4 small ones + 4 long ones + whole shape = 9 parallelograms	M1 A1 A1	M1 for considering different possibilities separately.
8	**Either** Total faces = 8 × 6 = 48 Visible faces = 5 × 4 = 20 Hidden = 48 − 20 = 28 **Or** Count hidden faces directly in a systematic way such as 8 + 8 + 8 + 4 or $(4 \times 3) + (4 \times 4)$.	M2A2	M1 for a logical approach. M1 for systematic method that could lead to a correct result. A1 for partially correct counting, for example, all the top (outside) bricks.
9	Area of one circle = 36π or $113(.09\ldots)$ Shaded area = $24 \times 24 - 4 \times 36\pi$ = 124 cm^2 $(123.610 \ldots)$	M1A1 M1A1 A1	M1 for using radius = 6. A1 for area of square M1 for subtraction. FT
10	5 ÷ 2 = 2.5 m circumference Radius = 2.5 ÷ π ÷ 2 OE = 0.40 m or 40 cm (0.397…)	M1A1 M1 A2	M1 for attempt to find circumference. Only A1 if calculator answer is seen but not rounded correctly to nearest cm or mm or if units are missing. FT from incorrect circumference.
11	**Either** The overlap is a trapezium. Lengths of parallel sides are 2 cm and 7 cm. Distance between them is 10 cm. Area = $\dfrac{2 + 7}{2} \times 10 = 45 \text{ cm}^2$ **Or** Find the area of trapezium that is not overlapping (105 cm^2) and subtract from the rectangle (150 cm^2).	M1 A1 A1 M1A1 QWC	M1 for stating it is a trapezium. The method must be shown to get full marks. Award marks in a similar way.

12a	**Either** Reflection and translation **Or** Reflection and rotation	M1	M1 for a valid pair.
	And An accurate description of the two transformations.	A2 QWC	There are lots of possible answers.
12b	**Either** An enlargement would change the size. **Or** A reflection must be included. OE	A1	Description will probably include diagrams. A clear explanation is required for full marks.
13	The shape is a prism of length 10 cm. **Either** Volume removed = area of triangle × 10 $= \frac{1}{2} \times 6 \times 3 \times 10 = 9 \times 10 = 90$ cm³. Volume remaining = 1000 − 90 = 910 cm³ **Or** Find that the area of the top is $100 - \frac{1}{2} \times 3 \times 6 = 91$ cm² and volume = 91 × 10 = 910 cm³.	A1 M2A2	M1A1 for area of triangle. M1A1 for finding the volume. Allow FT. Allow any equivalent method.
14	Show that $N = 3, 4, 5$ or 6 gives an integer angle. Then show that $N = 7$ does not.	M1A1 M1A1 QWC	For example, $N = 3, 4, 5$ or 6 gives the exterior angles as 120°, 90°, 72° and 60° or the interior angles as 60°, 90°, 108° and 120°. For example, show that the exterior angle, 360° ÷ 7, is not an integer.
15	$\pi \times 2.7^2$ $- \pi \times 2.3^2$ $= 6.3$ or 6.28 m²	M1A1 M1 A2	A1 for correct radius M1 for area formula used. M1 for subtracting areas, A1 if there is one arithmetic error. Do not award A2 unless the answer is rounded as shown and units are given. Allow an equivalent answer, for example, in cm².
16	Angle $A = \tan^{-1}\left(\dfrac{6}{8}\right) = 36.9°$. Length of BD = $8 \sin A = 4.8$ cm.	M1A2 M1A1	Allow FT. Allow any other valid method, for example, finding angle C and using that value, or finding AC by Pythagoras' theorem (10 cm) and using $BD \times AC = AB \times BC$.

17a	$10^2 + 24^2 = 26^2$	M1A1	
	So A must be a right angle (Pythagoras).		
	$15.6^2 + 20.8^2 = 26^2$		Knowledge of the fact that opposite angles of a cyclic quadrilateral add up to $180°$ must be shown.
	So B must be a right angle.	M1	
	$A + B = 180°$		
	So ABCD must be cyclic.	M1	
17b	Area of ABD + area of CDB	M1	
	$= \dfrac{1}{2} \times 10 \times 24 + \dfrac{1}{2} \times 15.6 \times 20.8$	A1	
	$= 120 + 162.24$		
	$= 282.24$ cm²	A1	Allow any accurate rounding.
18	$AC = 1.2 \div \sin 24° = 2.95$ m	M1A1	
	$AB = 4 - AC = 1.05$ m	M1A1	For A1, units must be given. Answer may be in cm.
19	Need to show that the angles of each triangle are the same sizes.	M1	Method mark for interpreting the word 'similar' correctly.
	Angle A is common to both triangles.	A1	
	Angle ADB = angle ACD (alternate segment theorem).	A1	
	Since the triangles have two angles that are equal, the third must also be equal (since the sum is $180°$ so they are similar.	A1	
20	Use the right-angled triangle with sides AB, 3 m and 20 m.	M1	
	$AB^2 = 3^2 + 20^2$	M1A1	
	$AB = \sqrt{409} = 20.2$ m or 20.22 m	A2	A1 for indicating the square root. A1 for correct rounding and units given.
21a	$\dfrac{\theta}{360} = \dfrac{4}{8\pi}$	M1A2	M1 for attempting to use the circumference of the circle. A1 for correct calculation for the circumference. A1 for any correct equation.
	$\theta = 57(.295…)°$	A1	Allow any rounding.
21b	Area $= \dfrac{\theta}{360} \times \pi \times 4^2$	M1A1	M1 for attempting to use the area of the circle.
	$= 8$ cm²	QWC	A1 for correct calculation for the area.
		A1	Answer should be exactly 8 but allow accurate FT from a rounded value of θ without penalty.

Q	Answer	Marks	Comments
22	**Either** Volume $= \frac{1}{3} \times \pi \times 5^2 \times 5 = \frac{125\pi}{3}$ If d cm is the depth when the glass is half full, that is also the radius of the top surface.	M1A1	Find the volume.
	$\frac{1}{3} \times \pi \times d^3 = \frac{125\pi}{6}$ $d^3 = \frac{125}{2}$	M1A1	Formulate a correct equation.
	$d = \sqrt[3]{\frac{125}{2}} = 3.968\ldots$ cm **Or** Use similar shapes to obtain: $\frac{d^3}{5^3} = \frac{1}{2}$ and solve this equation.	A2	A1 for finding a cube root, A1 for rounding correctly to 4 cm or 4.0 cm, with units. Allow answer of 40 mm. Up to 4 marks for the equation, 2 for the solution.

Statistics answers

Q	Answer	Marks	Comments
1	$\frac{8+4}{20} = \frac{12}{20}$	M1A1	
	$\frac{3}{5}$ or 0.6	A1	
2	$0.2 \times 50 = 10$	M1A1	You want losing, not winning tickets.
	$50 - 10 = 40$	A1	
	Or		
	$1 - 0.2 = 0.8$	M1A1	
	$0.8 \times 50 = 40$	A1	
3	Mean $= 196 \div 6 = 32.66\ldots$	M2A1	M1 for finding sum, M1 for dividing by 6.
	Closest is Amber.	A1	A1 for any correct rounding. Allow FT.
4	1 and 2, 2 and 4, 3 and 6 and the reverse of each.	M1A1	M1 for finding possible pairs. You could use an outcome space or a table of scores.
	$\frac{6}{36} = \frac{1}{6}$	M1A1	M1 for fraction. It must be simplified for A1. Allow a decimal (0.166...) or percentage, (16.6...%) correctly rounded.
5	Here is a possible table.	M1	M1 for a table with mass on one side and length on the other. They can be either way round.

	1.1–	1.2–	1.3–	1.4–	1.5–
20–					
25–					
30–					
35–					
40–					
45–					

Include the labels mass (kg) and height (m).

A3 — A1 + A1 for suitable groups on each side. The intervals can be different but they should be of equal size.
 A1 for clear labelling.

6a	0.08×5000	M1	
	$= 400$	A1	
6b	$7200 \div 0.08$	M1A1	M1 for any correct method.
	$= 90\,000$	A1	

7	Angles of the pie chart:	M1A2	M1 for correct method e.g. $360 \div 240 = 1.5$ to get multiplier.

Sector	Angle
Healthy	165°
Overweight	75°
Obese	30°
Underweight	90°

			A2 for correct calculation of angles.
			A1 if there is one error.
			A0 for more than one error.
		M1A2	A1 for correct angles.
		QWC	A1 for correct labelling. The chart must be neat and accurate to gain full marks.
			Full marks can be gained from an accurate pie chart, even if the angles and calculations are not seen.

8a	$38 + 2 \times 18 + 3 \times 6 + 4 \times 5 + 5 \times 2 + 7 \times 1 + 8 \times 2$	M1	
	$= 145$	A1	
8b	The mean is largest.	A1	
	The mode and the median are both 1.	A1	
	The mean must be larger than 1 because the mean must be between the smallest and largest i.e. between 1 and 8	A1	Only award this mark if the values of all three averages are discussed.
	Or		
	The mean is $145 \div 72 = 2.01\ldots$		There is no need to calculate the mean to get the mark.

9	Find the means of groups of three lengths (58, 54.3, 53 and 46.7 cm).	M2A1	M1 for finding the mean of a group of three, or equivalent.
	Or		
	Compare the total of three numbers with three times the fourth.		
	53 is the mean of the other three.	A1	

10	Find an average…	M1A2	M1 for using median or mean, A1 for each value. No mark for using the mode.
	either the medians (B: 41, G: 32)		
	or the means (B: $928 \div 22 = 42.2$, G: $714 \div 19 = 37.6$).		
	Comment on average: for example, the boys take longer, the median for the boys is 9 seconds more than the median for the girls,	A1 QWC	The comment should say who takes longer and by how much, on average.
	and		
	calculate a measure of spread…		
	either range (B: 46, G: 39)		
	or interquartile range (B: 20, G: 16).	M1A1	
	Comment on spread: for example, boys have greater variation in times, range for boys is 7 seconds more than range for girls.	A1 QWC	The explanations must be in clear English to gain full marks.
11	Two of the numbers must be 100.	A1	
	A third number must be 102 (to make the median 101).	A1	
	The fourth must be 106 (to make the mean 102).	M1A1 A1	M1 for total must be 408.
	Range is $106 - 100 = 6$.		
12	Morning total $= 3\frac{2}{3} \times 60 = 220$ minutes	M1A1	Award marks for answer in seconds (13 200).
	Afternoon total $= 4\frac{1}{3} \times 40 = 173\frac{1}{3}$ minutes.	A1	Or 10 400 seconds.
	Mean $= \dfrac{220 + 173\frac{1}{3}}{100} = 3$ minutes and 56 seconds.	M1A1	Or 236 seconds.
13	$0.45 + 0.75 - 1 = 0.2$	M2A1	The calculation must be seen to get the marks.
	Or	**or**	
	The probability of 4 or less is $1 - 0.45 = 0.55$	M1	
	and $0.75 - 0.55 = 0.2$.	M1A1	
	Or	**or**	
	The probability of 6 or more $= 1 - 0.75 = 0.25$	M1	
	and $0.45 - 0.25 = 0.2$.	M1A1	

14	Use **either** the mean **or** the median to say that on average the workers in A are 5 years younger than the workers in B, **and**	M1A1	M1 for using an average.
	use the interquartile range to say that there is less variation in the ages in factory A, **and**	M1A1 QWC	M1 for considering variation.
	make one other valid comparison, for example, comparing the percentage under 30.	A1 QWC	For full marks the comments in this question must be clearly and correctly written.
15	There is no correlation between Economics and Latin.	A1	All three pair of subjects must be compared to get full marks
	There is no correlation between Economics and Sociology.	A1	
	There is negative correlation between Latin and Sociology.	M1A1	M1 for sketching a graph or comments about the values indicating negative correlation, for example, high and low values paired.
16a	0.75×0.6	M1	
	$= 0.45$	A1	
16b	0.45×0.45	M1	Allow follow through from an incorrect answer to part **a**.
	$= 0.2025$ (or 0.203 or 0.20)	A1FT	
17	If ages are A, B and C, then $B + C = 38$; $A + C = 30$; $A + B = 28$. **Either…** add equations to get: $2A + 2B + 2C = 96$ and mean $= 96 \div 6 = 16$. **Or** Solve the equations to get: $A = 10$, $B = 18$, $C = 20$ and mean $= 48 \div 3 = 16$.	M1A1 M2A1 M1 for attempting to solve equations by any valid method.	M1 for forming any valid equations.
18	Find medians: boys 145, girls 153.	M1A1	
	Make a valid statement, for example, on average, girls are 8 cm taller than boys, **and**	A1 QWC	
	find interquartile ranges…	M1	Maximum of 2 marks for this section (out of a possible 4) if ranges are used instead of interquartile ranges. Ranges are 45 for both.
	Boys: $152 - 140 = 12$ cm	A1	
	Girls: $160 - 142 = 18$ cm	A1	
	Make a valid statement, for example, girls' heights are more varied than boys' heights.	A1 QWC	

19	 A curve passing through the five points (20, 0), (23, 25), (25, 50), (28, 75), (34, 100) as shown.	M2 A3	M1, A1 for axes. M1 for plotting five points. A2 for points, A1 if there is at most one error or omission.
20	Total number of people is 16 + 20 + 30 + 44 + 24 + 24 = 158 Number taking less than 30 minutes = 16 + 20 = 36 Percentage = 36 ÷ 158 × 100 = 23% or 22.8% or 23.78%.	M1 A1 A1 M1 A1	M1 for using scales to find frequencies.
21	The first one could be correct. The percentage in the class 1.75−1.79 is 92 ÷ 1260 = 7.5%. This means that 7.5% are 1.75 cm or more, so 4.7% could be more than 1.76 m. The cumulative frequencies are 157, 308, 660, 992, 1168, 1260. The lower quartile corresponds to a c.f. of 315 and is in the class 1.60−1.64. The upper quartile corresponds to a c.f. of 945 and is in the class 1.65−1.69. The IQR is the difference between values in each of these classes and cannot be more than 10 (1.695−1.595). The second statement must be false.	M1 A1 M1A1 M1A1	A1 for an accurate statement about percentage. M1 for a clear explanation. M1 for using cumulative frequencies. A1 for identifying the correct classes. A1 for finding greatest possible value for the IQR. M1 for a clear explanation.

Mixed questions answers

Q	Answer	Marks	Comments
1	A square can be attached to any of the four edges marked with a cross. 	M1A2	M1 for trying at least two different edges. A1 for three correct answers. Award the marks for any clear indication of where the square should go.

2	$16.50 \times 2 = 33.00$	M1A2	M1 for selecting the correct pair of prices.
	$11.75 \times 4 = 47.00$		A1 any correct part answer.
	Total is £80.00		A1 for final answer. Allow FT from an incorrect part answer.
			Do not penalise the lack of a £ sign.
3	**Either**		
	Add probabilities to get 0.0063		
	$0.0063 \times 65\,000 = 409.5$	M1A1	
	Round to 409 or 410 or 400.	A1	The answer must be rounded to a whole number to get the final mark.
	Or		Award marks in a similar way for any equivalent method.
	Multiply each probability by 65 000 to get 260, 97.5, 52 and add the results.		
4	15, 6, 0, −6, −15	M1A2	M1 for finding two different pairs of values.
			A1 for 3 or 4 correct answers.
5a	8 panels needed.	M1	Allow FT from an incorrect part answer.
	$27.45 \times 8 = 219.60$	A1	
5b	Delivery = 10% of 219.60 = 21.96	M1A1	Award full marks for a multiplier method to add 10%.
	Total = £241.56	A1	
6a	$(6 + 10 + 10 + 6 + 13) \div 5$	M1	
	$= 9$	A1	
6b	**Either**		In part **b** award marks in a similar way for any valid method. Some words or comment are required to get all three marks.
	Find the percentage for each day by dividing each height by 160.	M1	
	3.75%, 6.25%, 6.25%, 3.75%, 8.125%	A1	
	Target met on 4 days out of 5 because only Friday is above 7%.	A1	
	Or		
	Find 7% of 160 = 11.2		
	Met on 4 days out of 5 because only Friday is above 11.2.		
7	A*–C total = 24 + 28 + 30 + 44 = 126	A1	
	Percentage = $\dfrac{24}{126} \times 100 = 19\%$ or 19.0%.	M1A1	
8	Sale cost = $2 \times 22.95 + 2 \times 29.50$	A1	
	$= 104.90$		
	Original cost = $70 + 80 + 2 \times 90$		
	$= 330.00$	A1	
	Either		
	$(330 - 104.9) \div 330 \times 100 = 68(.2)\%$	M1A1	
	Or		
	$104.9 \div 330 \times 100 = 31.8\%$		
	and $100 - 31.8 = 68(.2)\%$		

9	$26\,178 - 25\,643 = 535$ units	A1	
	$535 \times 13.38 + 93 \times 14 = 8460.3$	M1A1	
	Cost = £84.60	A1	
10	The first digits will be 5 and 6.	M1	M1
	$632 \times 54 = 34\,128$	M1A1	M1 if sensible trials are seen.
			Other possibilities to try are
			$643 \times 52 = 33\,436$
			$642 \times 53 = 34\,026$
11	Stopping distance for car A = 94.	M1	Reading from the graph.
	Stopping distance for B = $94 \times 2 \div 3$ = 62.7.	A1	
	From graph, speed = 55 or 56 mph.	A1	
12	4 : 15	M1A2	M1 for attempting any valid method.
	Either		A1 for finding a ratio and A1 for simplifying it as much as possible.
	Rewrite one of both ratios to enable comparison, for example,		
	2 : 3 and 3 : 7.5; or 4 : 6 and 6 : 15; etc. and then simplify if necessary		
	Or		
	Choose an arbitrary number of goats.		
	for example, 20 goats $\Rightarrow$ 30 sheep $\Rightarrow$ 75 chickens and then simplify 20 : 75		
13	**Either**	M1A2	M1 for attempting to use the pattern number.
	Give a formula for the nth term i.e. $n(n + 1)$ or equivalent		A1 if the explanation is not clear.
	Or		
	Give an equivalent statement, for example, 'The pattern number multiplied by one more than the pattern number.'		
14	If the fractions are a and b $a + b = 1$ and $a - b = \dfrac{3}{4}$	M1	Any valid method.
	Solve, using any method.		
	The fractions are $\dfrac{1}{8}$ and $\dfrac{7}{8}$.	A2	A1 if only one is given.
15	The horizontal edges on the top add to a.	M1	M1 for analysing the horizontal edges and the vertical edges.
	Three vertical edges (excluding the one on the right) are $a + 2b$.	A1	
	The perimeter is $4a + 2b$.	A1	
16	Numbers for which 80% is a whole number are 5, 10, 15, ..., which are multiples of 5.	M1	Allow marks, even if LCM is not mentioned.
	Numbers for which 75% is a whole number are 4, 8, 12, ..., which are multiples of 4.	M1	
	Lowest common multiple is 20.	A1	

17	36 possible outcomes shown in a grid or table or list.	M1	
	15 outcomes where Jodi throws higher number $(5 + 4 + 3 + 2 + 1)$.	A1	
	$\dfrac{15}{36} = \dfrac{5}{12}$	A1	
18	Buy for $100 \div 1.09 = £91.74$. Paid back $100 \div 1.23 = £81.30$. Difference is £10.44.	M1 A2	M1 if a correct method is seen for either part. A1 if one of the part answers is incorrect but follow through is accurate.
19	List multiples of 6 and 7. Possible numbers are 12, 24, 36 and 48.	M1 A2	M1 if two lists of multiples are seen, even a partial one. A1 for at least three correct answer. No more that A1 if there is an incorrect answer.
20	$N = 14$ gives 105, the lowest three-digit one. $N = 44$ gives 990. $N = 45$ gives 1035, too large. From $N = 14$ to $N = 44$ is 31 three-digit triangular numbers.	M2 A2	M1 for substituting values correctly. M1 for looking for the largest and smallest. A1 for identifying either 14 for the lowest or 44 for the highest. A1 for 31.
21	No **Either** Consider areas. $69 \times 32 = 2208$ $300 \times 400 = 120\,000$ $120\,000 \div 2208 = 54.3$ which is more than 50. **Or** Look at a particular arrangement. For example, $300 \div 32$ and $400 \div 69$ which gives $9.375 \times 5.80 = 54.3\ldots$ which is more than 50.	M2A2	0 marks if there is no explanation. M1 for using areas. A1 for one correct area. M1 for division. A1 for correct conclusion. Or M1 A1 for correct analysis of one side. M1 for using the values found. A1 for conclusion. Award marks for analysis of any other possible arrangement.

22	Use proportions. $2508.80 \div 2450 = 1.024$ $3055 \times 1.024 = (£)3128.32$ **Or** Find percentage increase is 2.4%. And then increase 3055 by 2.4%, using any valid method. **Or** Any other valid method, for example $3055 \div 2450 \times 2508.8$	M1A2 M1A1 A1 Or M1A1 A1	Only M1A1 if method is correct but there are rounding errors. Award marks in a similar way for any other valid method.
23	Use any point to give a width and corresponding area, for example, 3 and 30. Divide to find the length for example, $30 \div 3 = 10$ Add length and width and double to find the perimeter, for example, $2(3 + 10)$ Answer is 26 cm	M1 A1 M1 A1	 A0 if units are not included.
24	36 brown cows and 24 white 24 brown and 18 white less than one year. $\dfrac{42}{60} = \dfrac{7}{10}$	M1A1 A1 A2	M1 for simultaneous equation or any other valid method. A1 if both numbers are correct. Allow FT from incorrect previous answers. Only A1 if fraction is not as simple as possible.
25	Not safe. **Either** 100 km/h = $\dfrac{100 \times 1000}{60 \times 60}$ = 27.8 m/s $\dfrac{40}{27.8}$ = 1.4 seconds which is less than 2. **Or** 100 km/h = $\dfrac{100 \times 1000}{60 \times 30}$ = 55.6 m in 2 s which is longer than 40 m.	M2A2 M1A1 M1A1 Or M2A1 A1	0 marks if there is no reason. Explanation required to get the A1. Or
26	First volume = $\pi \times 10^2 \times 10$ $= 1000\pi$ or 3142 cm³ Second volume = $\pi \times 5^2 \times 20$ $= 500\pi$ or 1571 cm³ The first volume is double the second.	M1A1 A1 A1	M1 for using the volume formula correctly in either case. A1 for any equivalent description but some comment is required to get this mark. Allow FT from a previous incorrect volume.

27	**Either**		
	$R + S = 61$	M1	M1 for formulating equations.
	$S + T = 89$		
	$T + R = 76$		
	Add all three: $2R + 2S + 2T = 226$		
	$R + S + T = 113$	M1A1	M1 for any attempt to solve the equations.
	Or		
	Find individual ages and use those.		
	They are $R = 24$, $S = 37$, $T = 52$		
28	Lasagne $588 \times \dfrac{5}{4} = 735$	M1A1	M1 if a valid method of finding the number of calories is seen in either case.
	Banana $144 \times \dfrac{4}{3} = 192$	A1	
	$735 + 192 + 142 = 1069$	A1	
29	For X, look at multiples of 3, down from 100.	M2A2	M1 for looking at large multiple of X.
	99, 96, 93, 90, 87, 84, 81...		A1 for any lists of multiples.
	Look at multiples of 5 and 7 to make it up to 100.		M1 for ruling out any numbers.
	81 is the answer.		A1
30	Suppose the length of one card is x.		
	$x + (x - 50) + x = 205$	M1A1	M1 for using algebra, A1 for a valid equation.
	Or		
	$(x - 25) + x + (x - 25) = 205$		
	$3x - 50 = 205$	M1	M1 for solving the equation.
	$3x = 255$		
	$x = 85$		
	Length is 85 mm.	A1	A0 if units are missing.
31	$A = \pi r^2$ and $C = 2\pi r$	M1	M1 for using these two formulae.
	Rearrange these to show the required result, for example,	A1	A1 for any appropriate substitution.
	$\dfrac{C^2}{4\pi} = \dfrac{4\pi^2 r^2}{4\pi} = \pi r^2 = A$	M1A1	M1A1 for further valid algebra.
	Or		Or
	$4\pi A = 4\pi \times \pi r^2 = (2\pi r)^2 = C^2$		Award marks in a similar way for any other method.
	and the result follows.		
	Or		
	Any other valid algebraic manipulation.		

32	Draw a triangle, using the centre of the circle, for example,	M1A1	M1 for use of a suitable triangle. A1 for using a trigonometric function.
	Radius = $\dfrac{5}{\cos 30°}$ = 5.7735	A1	
	$C = 2 \times \pi \times 5.7735 = 36.275...$	M1	FT from an incorrect value.
	Round to 36 or 36.3 or 36.28 cm.	A1	Condone lack of units in this case.
33	2.39×10^8 m	M1	M1 for converting to same units.
	$(2.39 \times 10^8) \div (3.00 \times 10^8) = 0.80$ s	M1A1	
	Or		
	Convert both distances to km.		
	$(2.39 \times 10^5) \div (3.00 \times 10^5) = 0.80$ s		
34	$500 = \dfrac{\pi d^3}{12} \Rightarrow d^3 = \dfrac{500 \times 12}{\pi}$ $= 1909.9$	M1A1	M1 for substituting and attempting to rearrange.
	$d = \sqrt[3]{1909.9} = 12.4$		
	Diameter is 12.4 cm	A1	
35	$AB = \dfrac{15}{\tan 20°} = 41.2$	M1A1	
	$AC = 41.2 + 30 = 71.2$	A1	FT from an incorrect value.
	Height of tree at C = 71.2 tan 20°	M1	
	$= 25.8$ m or 25.9 m	A1	Allow rounding to 26 m.
36	Form two equations, for example,	M1A1	M1A1 for forming two equations.
	$2s + 4o = 2$		
	$3s + 3o = 9$		
	Solve equations, using any method, for example, simplify to $s + 2o = 1$ and $s + o = 3$ and find o first.	M1	If o is taken to be positive, the coefficients of o will be negative. M1 for an attempt to solve them.
	Points for a six $(s) = 5$	A1	Value of o (−2 for these equations) is not required.

37	The exterior angle is $360° \div 12 = 30°$. **Or** the interior angle is $10 \times 180° \div 12 = 150°$ so the exterior angle is $30°$. **And** The angle at A is two exterior angles $= 60°$. AB and AC are the same length because the polygons are congruent. The triangle is isosceles and hence the other two angles are also $60°$. It is equilateral.	M1A1 A1 A1 A1	M1A1 for showing the exterior angle is $150°$ by any method.
38	**Either** Use Pythagoras' theorem to find the side of the square: $s^2 + s^2 = d^2$ $2s^2 = d^2$ The area of the square is s^2 so the result follows. **Or** Show that the square can be made into a rectangle, for example: Area of rectangle $= \frac{1}{2}\, d \times d = d^2$.	M1A1 M1A1 Or M1A1 M1A1	M1A1 for any use of Pythagoras' theorem. M1A1 for any convincing diagram.
39	Total number of women $= \dfrac{30}{0.12} = 250$ Total number of men $= \dfrac{3}{5} \times 250 = 150$ 10% of $150 = 15$.	M1A1 M1A1 A1	M1 for any valid method.
40	$BD = 10 \div \cos 45° = 14.14$ $BE = 14.14 \div \cos 45° = 20$ $BF = 20 \div \cos 45° = 28.28$ $AB = 28.28 \div \cos 45° = 40$ **Or** After finding BE, use the fact that ABEF is an enlargement of EBCD with a scale factor of 2, so $AB = 2BE = 40$ **Or** Use Pythagoras' thoerem repeatedly. $BD = \sqrt{10^2 + 10^2} = \sqrt{200}$ $BE = \sqrt{200 + 200} = \sqrt{400} = 20$ $BF = \sqrt{800}$ $AB = \sqrt{1600} = 40$	M1A1 M1 A1 Or M1A1 M1 A1	For finding BD. For finding further sides.